from
these
shores

FROM THESE SHORES

by
Helga Skogsbergh
illustrated by
Roger W. Palmquist

Published by COVENANT PRESS Chicago
1963

FROM THESE SHORES

Printed in the United States of America

to my children:

BETTY

MARY

SAM

CONTENTS

AUTHOR'S PREFACE

A ripe moon hangs high in the sky. Its gold streams through the heavy green of the elms outside the windows of my secluded nook in the attic where I sit. It is midnight, and the glaring lights of the city are beginning to dim, enough so that now and then a star comes through the dark meadows of the sky. The tumult in the street has subsided, and for a few brief hours night sheds its healing balm on the tensions gathered during the day. In these rare moments I have picked up my pen again and will go on from where I left off, nearly three autumns ago.

As a child exclaims in disappointment when the story he is told seems too brief, so many of the readers of my last book, *Comes the Day, Comes a Way,* expressed regret that the pioneer narrative ended too soon.

Thus the story shall go on. In the relentless march of "progress" the frontier scene must never fade. As our civilization advances, we need all the more to look back to a generation which knew simplicity and stillness, starlight, sunsets, and seascape tones—a world removed from the clutter and frustrations of an age where multitudes are destroying themselves.

It is good to unlock again the chest of childhood memories wherein are tapestries woven from the fabrics of early sensations—joy, tears, struggle. Interwoven are the exalted moments when the hand of heaven swept across the strings of earth and life swelled with wonder.

In the frontier drama are many sturdy scenes—from the day when the pioneer sets his foot on the spade and pushes it into the deep, raw earth until his task is finished and he steps off life's stage. Weary, but bearing the dignity of one who has truly given, he yields to the quiet bosom of the same good earth with whom he has long companioned.

Though the chapters in this book are not all in chronological order, and are occasionally sprinkled with dashes of fiction, each is a true incident, told as best I can remember.

And now up here in my sanctuary beneath the roof I must be on with my story while the night is still and the city sleeps.

HELGA SKOGSBERGH

Minneapolis, Minnesota

Spring, 1963

from
these
shores

to the reader:

Many of the Swedish words and phrases which appear throughout the text are self-explanatory. Some, however, require definition, and a glossary, giving the English equivalents of all Swedish expressions, will be found on pages 161-164.

1. Hitherto

The land slopes down to the gray waters of the Great Lake and has nothing more to say. The tall forest of Wisconsin's early history halts and bows reverently to the majestic Gitche Gume, whose song is never silent. In it dwells the agony and hope of the ages, for the sagas that are cradled in its breast are many. While earth shall last, it will ever be the same. The line of the horizon lies unbroken, save for a heavily-laden lumber boat or the dark streak of a scow basking in solitude.

Across the heavens at night, streamers of Northern Lights shimmer and flare, and myriad stars leave a man rooted in his tracks. One reads the evangel of God's creation from the tiniest, star-petaled flower to the towering firs hallowing the shores with their many spires. On these shores mystery and majesty go hand in hand.

On the gull-swept borderland one listens to a strange calling, a calling which has never found utterance in words, something too profound for answer, and man's littleness cries out in tongueless wonder—"How great Thou art!"

Here when the dial of time flashed from the '80s to the '90s, a fragment of frontier history began. Washed up on these shores came a handful of immigrants, each with the stamp of Sweden set firmly on his speech and action. With empty purses, a will to work, and an unshakeable faith in God, they set themselves to the task of carving out a civilization, half-way up the coast of northern Wisconsin, and soon the wilderness resounded from the blow of ax and falling timber.

Among the first to hew their way into this primeval scene were Papa and Mama Hanson and their infant daughter, Ingrid. Accompanying them were their friends—Isakson, his wife Emma, and their little ones, Annie and Isak. Seven there were, counting great and small—seven, the perfect number.

Like seeds flung on untilled ground, they struggled to take root. Felled trees and huge brush piles of withering boughs gave evidence of the first footprints of civilization. Amid dense circles of wilderness two little log huts began to breathe, and from low cabin roofs warm curls of smoke rose skyward, signaling direction to an occasional land seeker—"Look, here is life!" . . . . . *Ja,* that was then.

* * *

Several years have passed. The road of frontier trudging is beginning to show tracks. Not so often now does man need carry a feed sack on his back or tramp his own trail to find a distant neighbor. *Ja,* think, now there are horses, a mule team here and there, perhaps a pair of oxen. The squeak of wagon wheels on roads more widely slashed and firmly packed is music to the ear.

"*Ja,* hitherto has the grace of God been with us," says Papa Hanson, paying a visit to his neighbor Isakson in the fields. Man to man they meet across the line where claim meets claim. One has to talk to someone.

Settling down on stumps of Norway pine just inside Isakson's clearing, they indulge in a brief rest from their spring hoeing, their old straw hats shoved down to hide the glare of the afternoon sun. *Ack,* it is good to ease one's back and wipe the perspiration from sun-tanned necks. And as they sit there conversing about rain and crops and needed farm machinery, and arguing out the trend of world events—the little they knew—who should they see coming up the field but Emma—Isakson's Emma. And she is carrying a pot of coffee in one hand and a basket in the other. To be sure, it's coffee time, the sun already part way to the west. Setting her things down on a stump beside the men, she turns to go.

"I must hurry back and see after the cows," she says. "They seem set on getting into the garden patch." With that she leaves, her long, full skirt trailing in the grass.

Isakson lifts the cloth off the basket and studies the contents. *Ja visst,* there's enough for two. Emma must have seen Papa on the other stump when she prepared. Two cups in the basket and breads wrapped up in a cotton napkin, a few molasses cookies, and a pot of steaming coffee. *Ja,* plenty for two and to spare. That Emma, with her plump, generous hand. And what is more refreshing than four o'clock coffee in the field?

Isakson hands the basket over to Papa Hanson. "Be so good and have a 'sam-vish,' " he says.

" 'Sam-vish,' is that what the Americans call *smörgås?*" asks Papa, helping himself to two slices of rye bread with a cut of partridge meat between. " 'Sam-vish'—I think I can learn to say that myself. You are not so dumb in English, Isakson, for the short time you have been in America." Papa raises his bearded upper lip and takes a deep bite. His neighbor punctuates the compliment with a nod of self-satisfaction.

Four-o'clock coffee in the field, under a large sky, the waves below breaking quietly in long rolls upon the beach, trees casting cool shadows on the sun-drenched meadow, the fragrance of upturned soil and greening bush—*ack,* how could one ask for more! It is a great moment in the summer day—coffee in the field.

"*Ja,* as you say," says Isakson, "so far has God's grace been with us." It comes natural to sing praises at a time like this.

"And do you know we have another neighbor south of us?" asks Papa, pointing to the wooded slope behind their clearings.

"*Ja visst,* have I knowed that. They say his name is Johnson. Another Johnson. Haven't I heard his ax go chop, chop early in the morning, and seen the smoke curl up among the trees in the evening?"

So other settlers are creeping into the laps of land and forest farther in from shore. Things are looking forward now.

Solitude and isolation—*ja,* that still clings to the countryside, but now there are ways of getting in, and out, and around. Roads have begun to line the territory like a spider's first web. Some are taut and straight, some twice the length they should be, meandering as they do around sloughs, ravines, and ponds, for it is yet not time for spanning bridges. But roads there are anyhow. Some are open, wind-swept ways, some sheltered by tall walls of spruce and pine which never cease their soughing night or day. There are roadsteads which rise and fall and curve as though playing a game with the traveler. But even so there is fascination in wondering what lies up ahead beyond the hill and around the bend.

"What a comfort is a road," says Isakson, swallowing the last drop of coffee in his cup.

"A road that leads to a journey's purpose," answers Papa, looking thoughtfully into the glowing west.

And so they chat a little more, looking backward across the seedtimes and the harvests that have seen them thus far—Papa and Isakson—neighbors as they are.

Ja, things have been going forward not so little. Now the frugal clearings are becoming lush little fields of oats and corn and alfalfa ripening in the full sun. Men plough and plant and sigh a prayer over their fields. Women wait and work and give birth. Oh, there is still loneliness, and longing for the land they left behind—Sweden. There have been crop failures, leaving flat purses in the pockets of their faded overalls; illness, not so little, and even death has laid its solemn hand upon the settlement, man and beast alike. *Ack,* hadn't Papa nailed together several coffins in his little carpenter shed behind the house? And one could also speak of lesser trials that never seemed to lift: the howl of wolves on winter nights, enormous bear tracks in the garden patch, the peas and carrots eaten up by bear or hare, the disappearance of the choicest hen with only a mound of feathers left to tell the tale.

But should some traveler stop at Mama Hanson's door and say, "How you like it here?" she would rise up and smile and say with strength, "Worse days could one well see."

No, there is nothing to do but go on and try to weave some hope into their conversations when they chance to meet.

"Tomorrow it will be better." In spite of dark circumstances, Mama could remember no time when the power to say "tomorrow" was really lost, whether it referred to the day ahead, or the year, or to the life beyond this earthly pilgrimage. In the tomorrow the meaning of yesterday and today would be made plain. *Ack,* what a tower of hope is the word "tomorrow."

And always a brighter day does come, opening like a lovely morning glory with rising sun and skies of blue and healing in its wings. *Ja,* there are respites when the world about them seems to reach perfection, when the fog lifts and they view their lot from the holiest heights of the spirit. Rare moments, like a gold thread amid coarse homespun, like a star at night, the brighter for the darkness that surrounds it. Against the backdrop of their rugged existence there are mornings when the forest rings with happy hallelujahs, and evenings when God spreads His great amen upon the hush of land and sea.

"*Ja,* it is good to look back," says Isakson, as he gathers the coffee cups in the empty basket.

Back in his own cornfield, Papa resumes his hoeing, and while he tills the soil, he holds conversation with himself. There are so many matters on his mind.

Then suddenly he is aware of children down below, with high-pitched gladness in their voices. Annie, Isak, Ingrid, playing on the shores, of course.

Likely they are building houses in the sand, he thinks; houses and farms and little hamlets, whichever way their fancy turns. How often he had seen these sprawling habitations on the beach, with roads, sand fences, leafy twigs for trees, and little hand-dug wells with water seeping through. And over all were fingerprints, little ones and bigger ones, eagerly carrying out the suggestions of the imagination. But he had also seen the labor of a day washed away in some dark moment of the night by the relentless billows. There had followed bitter disappointment, but in another day or so young spirits had set to work again, a little wiser, and more cautiously had built their sand encampment farther from the water's edge. Always they tried again. *Ack, ja,* what lessons in life there are to learn from these shores.

2. Anders

That year winter came on the heels of a radiant Indian summer. The shortened days with their note of melancholy dragged into longer ones with the sharp sting of mid-winter set firmly upon them. The February snows lay heavy, and the little settlement on the shores was locked in crystal and alabaster.

And in the hush of a winter twilight a baby boy was born. Time it was for another child to enter the Hanson household. Isaksons had four now, but Mama had lost her second child—three years before. That was the first death in the settlement, and the little mound up in the sapling meadow could still be seen from her south window.

In the nine months of carrying close to her heart her third baby, Mama Hanson had become acquainted with her unborn son. Often she felt definite intimations regarding his future.

"You know, Emma," she explained, when on a white December morning she met her neighbor while shoveling snow along the path between the two log cabins, "my unborn child will be a man of the soil, one who will wrestle with stumps and roots and weather. He's already so strong."

"Are you sure about that? He may want to be a fisherman, or a carpenter, or even a minister." Emma tossed a shovel of snow to the mounting banks and paused to catch her second wind. Emma, too, had begun another pregnancy. Things were moving fast along the shores.

"If you could feel the sturdy movements inside of me, you would agree. He is one who will take the wilderness by the horns. That's the way it feels. Anders—that's what Papa wants to name him—will be a friend of the good earth. When I think of Papa," continued Mama, leaning on her shovel, "why, he is already showing the marks of toil and hardship. You know he was never a robust one, like your Isakson. It is fitting that he should have a son, for by the time Anders reaches early manhood, Papa will be an old man. No, I think his coming is as it is s'posed to be!" Mama lifted her shovel from the drift and resumed her task.

"You may have right," nodded Emma. "That is the way I feel sometimes about our Isak. A friend of the soil, stable, loyal, someone to hold down the stakes."

"*Ja*, now the path is open again till the next snowstorm, which will come soon enough. With the men in the lumber camps this will be our winter chore." Mama straightened her back and looked the path over in both directions. It was neat and friendly, as it should always be. The frosted bushes along the way sparkled in the morning sunshine. Every fir tree held soft pillows of snow on its branches. The countryside glistened like a rich, enchanted fairyland.

"Think, anyway, how beautiful winter can be, in spite of its sternness," said Emma, pausing in deep wonder.

"This time it is your turn to come over to my house for coffee," said Mama, with no ifs or buts, as she picked up her shovel to go. "I want to read you the letter I got from sister Augusta. You have your Annie to see after the younger ones. Set your shovel in the drift and come."

"*Nej,* what say you—a letter from Augusta? It can't be that she is coming to the shores in the dead of winter?" There must be something special when a letter comes this time of year, thought Emma, as she walked behind Mama in obedient, single-file manner, the path just wide enough for one. The midmorning sun struck against the winter whiteness till their eyes filled with tears.

There was warmth in Mama's kitchen. Homemade rugs with splashes of color lay neatly on the wide-planked floors, newly scrubbed. A tea kettle hummed on the back of the wood stove, and a fire still crackled in the grate. The woodbox stood pleasantly filled with wood, and the smell of birch was strong and good. Ingrid, in the other room, was happily sketching a pine tree with a thick lead pencil given her by Bachelor Guldstrand up on Flag River Road. Here was contentment, a feeling that belonged to a winter day, thought Emma, as she slipped off her shawl and with one corner of her apron wiped the snow-tears from her eyes.

Over the steaming cups of Arbuckle's coffee, Mama

read Augusta's letter. Augusta was Mama's younger sister. She had come from Sweden in recent years and was now serving as hired girl in a fashionable home in the Big City across the lake. What she hadn't learned in America! Her letter began:

> Dear Betty:
>
> I got your letter with the sad news. So you are going to have another one. That is too bad. I should think one young one should be enough, living as you do far off in the wilds with so little to do with. But I shall come up there and be with you while you are in childbed. However, I will not be midwife. That I can tell you. Your good neighbor, Emma, can take care of that. I will keep the fires and the coffeepot going and add some laughs to the gloomy hours. Let me know when you want me.
>
> Augusta

Jojomen, it won't be so bad to have Augusta around at that time," said Emma, with brightness. "She puts life in us poor homestead women."

"And spunk, too," added Mama. "*Ruter.*"

Augusta's arrivals were always happy affairs. Five-year-old Ingrid couldn't wait for Anders to be born. Along with her aunt's coming would be mysterious bags and parcels from the Big City. Curious pieces of fruit called oranges—*apelsiner*—were sure to show up. How she longed for these fragrant globes of gold that came from some sunny Eden far away. Along with the *apelsiner* were other miracles: bananas! grapes! plums! From another bag would come cookies, frosted in white, with chocolate outlines of George Washington's face, or Abraham Lincoln's—you could take your pick. One looked long at the noble faces before taking a bite. They were memorable occasions, these visits of Aunt Augusta.

The days of February seemed especially long that year, but when Aunt Augusta finally arrived, a few days before Anders came, the log cabin on the shores broke out with laughter. Augusta knew how to tell funny stories, how to impersonate, how to fling an act in the most unexpected moment. Sometimes, when she was sure Papa was in the barn or up in the woods, she would grab Ingrid and dance across the kitchen floor singing:

Å så väva vi vamman
Å så slå vi tillsamman.

Emma and Mama were especially interested in the skit she produced where a stylish American lady interviews a hired girl fresh from Sweden. Augusta was not afraid to speak up. She was a good worker and in demand. She didn't need to take everything. *Nej, du.* She could answer them. Augusta had a mouth.

Even Emma, who wasn't much for laughter, couldn't resist the temptation to steal over to the other cabin when Augusta was there. She was hungry for the thing she had tried to hold back—a little fun. And who could resist the warmth of a bit of laughter on a cold winter day, isolated as they were in a snow-blocked world. "*Ja, tacka för de.*" What with coffee on the stove and Augusta acting the part of a fancy American lady, Mama's log house became a magnet. It was hard for Emma to stay away. Only Papa cutting birch in the upper woodlot missed the comedies going on in the little log house down by the shores. He had come home from the logging camp for a few days to cut wood.

"And it is best so," said Mama, keeping an eye on

the south window. "Women need to set aside some part of their lives away from their men." Papa was not much for frivolity—*slarv,* he called it. Comfort the comfortless, that he could; and weep with the mourner; but to laugh with the laughers—*ja,* that was another thing.

The day Anders had decided on his journey to earth there was no jesting, you can be sure. Augusta, excited and breathless, ran over to Emma's cabin and knocked fiercely on her door. Knocks on one's door in the dead of winter were, even yet, rare events, so Emma guessed what was in the offing.

"Her time has come, Emma; hurry up," panted Augusta. "I'll stay here with your little ones till the storm is over."

Emma slipped into her long boots, wrapped up a pan of fresh rolls, and prepared to go.

"You'll find coffee on the top shelf," she told Augusta, "and *kringlor* in the large lard can on the floor." She threw on her shawl and started windward for Hanson's log house.

"You see to it that Hanson stays in the house with you when the baby comes," yelled Augusta as Emma flew down the path. "Men should know what a wife goes through on 'count of them." Emma called back something, but Augusta couldn't hear what it was.

Papa opened the door for Emma and had a good fire going and hot water on the stove. It was midafternoon, and Mama was able to enjoy a cup of strong coffee with Emma. Clean rags and string were laid out, and everything was in readiness for the newcomer.

Papa stood ready to do any errand that Emma suggested. "Strange what a meek and obedient frame of mind a man has at such a time as this," said Mama, while Papa went to the woodshed for some heavy chunks of birch. In the kitchen he had held Ingrid's interest by having her watch him half-sole a pair of old shoes.

"*Ja,* Emma, I remember when your Ester was born, our first arrival on these shores. How little we knew and how frightened we were."

"*Ack,* talk never about that," said Emma, her thoughts going back to that first year of homesteading. "I remember what you said when you came over, Betty. 'God is our refuge and strength.' And in that strength it went. *Ja,* think anyway."

It was nearing five o'clock that afternoon when Anders was born. All had gone well, and Mama was resting peacefully, her newly-born son in her arms. Through the west window she saw that the snowing had stopped and that a pale glow of sun finished the day. Emma was lighting another kerosene lamp, for dusk came speedily. How good to have Emma; except for her, there was no neighbor on a winter day.

"Isn't it strange, Emma, that our babies seem to come in the end of the day. So did your Ester, and so did Palmers' Elsie. What can that mean, do you suppose?" Mama drew a deep sigh.

"It means simply that the next generation will take over when our day is nearing its end," said Emma, for want of something to answer and feeling it was not so dumb a piece of wisdom on a moment's notice.

Childbirth was becoming more frequent now in the settlement since more families had moved in. Little by little the fear of the ordeal was lessening, in spite of the lack of skilled help and medical aids. A woman gave birth. Nothing out of the natural course. It is given to her to give birth. A frontier woman accepts this assignment as she accepts all others. She ultimately learns to overcome all fears. What is more, Mama and Emma were becoming quite skilled in the practice of midwifery.

More than once, in the dead of night, one or the other would be called to the bedside of some settler's wife up in the wooded hills or even in the town. Childbirth? That was a minor role in the pioneer drama. Nothing to make a mountain of. *Nej, för all del.*

Papa, standing close beside the bed, beamed with pride at the husky infant pressed warmly against Mama's breast.

"To think we have a son at last," he sighed, with a deep sense of fulfillment. "It is a man's great moment to look upon his son, his first-born son. May he be worthy of his honorable name—Andreas," and Papa's mind withdrew to the ancient apostle by the Sea of Galilee.

"It is a thing of note to be born and reared beside a great body of water, to hear its whisperings, its call, to feel its strength."

The day was nearing its end when Emma threw on her shawl to leave, her task now finished.

"*Ja,* now this is over," she said, giving Mama a pat on the shoulder. "Now I must go home to see after my own. I will come over tomorrow, and you have Augusta to help you."

As she trudged through the snow in the darkness that rounded out the evening, her thoughts were deep thoughts. Another child had been born, another pair of bare feet to leave their prints in the summer sands. And this was not the end, for Emma, herself, would be next. After that, how many more? *Ja,* say that. Emma wondered.

As Papa walked to the stable that night, he thought of his son. He saw him as a man, full-grown, a man loved and respected by his fellow men, his sturdy hands skilled to do many things, his soul strong to face life. And in the dark of the evening, from the deep well of his soul, he drew a prayer and blessed the gift of this day.

Little Ingrid looked upon her little brother, and a new facet of feeling was added to her store. She drew on her gray flannel coat and walked out into the night. Under the stars in the light of a dim moon she could think better. The little inner room in her life was beginning to expand with strange elusive stirrings. Across the frozen waters, over that magic circle of woods surrounding the clearing, came a whisper again. She could not explain what she felt, but she knew it held the power to remain forever.

It was late in the night when Mama drew aside the curtain and looked out of the window. Silently it had begun to snow again. At the edge of the clearing where Baby Ruth lay, the wild cherry thicket was a miracle of white, as if it were in blossom. A new mask of white was sealing up the old. Winter. Who can understand winter? One can see the purposes and intentions of spring and summer and autumn. But winter—what a mystery.

And birth goes on, regardless of season. Mama drew her infant son close to her breast and fell into the sleep of complete exhaustion. It had been a day of great accomplishment on the shores.

3. Klovstad's store

The sun smiled upon a mild April morning. Winter had loosened its grip on the wilderness, and snowdrifts had shriveled into crusts and frayed away. The frost oozed from the soil, releasing the odors that had been locked in all winter, an earthly scent which somehow stirs the senses.

"*Ja*, today is the day I have to go to Klovstad's store," announced Mama, vigorously stirring the oatmeal on the stove. Papa had finished his work in the logging camp and would be spending the next three seasons at home on the farm.

"I'm taking Ingrid with me," she added. "She needs to get out among people, especially if she starts school in the fall. You know how folk-shy she is."

"Who's going to see after Anders?" asked Papa, amazed at Mama's spirit of independence. He could tell Augusta had been around not so far back.

"Anders is a good baby," reminded Mama, "and you said last night you would be spending the day filling the cracks between the logs of the cabin. That means you will be close at hand." Mama jerked open the door to the narrow attic stairway.

"Up with you now, Ingrid," she said. "*Morgonstund har guld i mun.* You shall go with me to Klovstad's store today."

The prospect of going away with Mama, especially to town, was well worth the discomfort of getting out of the warm blankets. The place called Town, hewn out of the thick timberland only a few years before, had quietly sprung into a good-sized patch of living. Like toys scattered by children, the buildings stood one here, and one there, along the well-tramped roads. With the logging and lumber industry expanding, more people were trickling into the community. It could now boast of three little stores, a post office, a large saw mill, and two churches. One was a white-painted building where the Lutherans worshipped. Its dignity was enhanced by a tall steeple, and there was talk of someday hanging a bell in the little belfry. *Ack,* that was going to be something to listen to! The other church stood plain and steepleless over on a lonely edge of town. Here was where Pastor Rodin held forth with his handful of Mission Friends when he came to town. This was where the Isaksons and Hansons worshipped.

Along the center road of town were family dwellings of various shapes and sizes. Small tar-paper shacks spoke of contented bachelorhood. Only a few houses were turned to make the most of the lakeward view, their windows looking out upon the harbor and the ships that moved across the immense waters.

Ja, the trip to town was no ordinary event. In no time Ingrid was down in the kitchen, ready to go.

"So you have set your mind to go to town," said Papa, as he watched Mama pack her prints of butter in the handwoven basket. "Why don't you trade at one of the other stores? Johnson and Nelson will take your butter and eggs. Always you go to Klovstad. All I hear when you come back is 'Klovstad, Klovstad.' "

"*Ja,* say that." Mama turned from the stove to pick up baby Anders. "That I can tell you why. I not only like Klovstads, but there I can get a good cup of coffee when I'm done trading. When you've walked that long, windy Corduroy Road, you should know the smell of coffee isn't so little inviting. No, give me Klovstad's store."

Many were the times Mama walked the two and one-half miles to town. It was a pleasant experience. Somehow anxious living blew away, and a lighter mood took over. There was a young feeling that came over her.

"It's like getting out of a cage for a couple of hours," she told Ingrid as they entered the road that led into the deep woods. The winding road, walled on both sides by fragrant pine and spruce, was a comfortable place in which to grow chatty if you had a traveling companion, and a most delightful place for weaving your favorite dream if you were alone.

"Strange, what a walk through this woods will do for you," said Mama, crossing the road to walk on the less sunny side. "You get so tired of having no place to go but to the stable or the hen house. *Ja,* think. Here is peace, no wind, no sound of waves. Here I can dump my anxieties right into the lap of the woods and come away lighthearted and free." Ingrid felt she understood, for she knew already in a child's way the strange power of renewal this road through the woods had.

For a time they trudged on in silence, each thinking her own thoughts.

"Can't we sit down on this log and rest a while," suggested Ingrid, feeling a bit weary from the weight of the basket of eggs she was carrying.

"We can imagine we are stopping at a neighbor's house," she said. "Let's play 'pretend,' like we do sometimes." Resting on a log by the side of a road is a special kind of delight. Ingrid had several such logs on the way to town, and Mama was not disinclined to pamper herself a bit on these occasions.

And what fun it was to pretend. Strange, how often they imagined there were neighbors. It is the way of frontier women and children to dream of neighbors—other people—thought Mama. There were many little haunts in the woods where Ingrid, Annie, and Isak played with imaginary people. Every haunt had a family name. Here they mingled and rejoiced with boys and girls their own age—Daniel, Joseph, Sofie, Julia. There was even a little church in the thicket, and how wonderful it was to play church and take turns being organist, or minister, or just plain listener.

"*Ja,* imagination is a powerful thing," said Mama, as they paused to rest on a mossy log along the way. "Keep it alive always, Ingrid. It will brighten many a cloudy day up ahead. My, this is a beautiful morning! The kind of morning that sets the wheels inside of you going as if they were newly greased."

Mama stooped to pull a crawling vine near the

log, and hidden beneath it was an early pink arbutus, fragrant as heaven itself. "*Ja, ack, ack,* what beauty lies hidden in a woods." A robin was practicing a difficult twirl in a nearby maple. Again and again he repeated the phrase, but with seeming difficulty. "*Ja,* you are getting there," called Mama. "*Han som hänger i vinner.*"

Ingrid knew there were many sides to Mama's nature. She liked her best as she was this morning—young and playful. But Mama was usually too busy and too practical to spend much time in playing make-believe with her. Only once in a while would she let herself accompany Ingrid on these fanciful excursions.

There were happy things they fashioned for themselves that morning while they sat on the log in the forest shade.

"Let's pretend we have a six-room house like the Johnsons in town are building. And we are going to buy some nice things to put in it," said Ingrid, enjoying the luxury of this rare moment.

"And our house won't be made of logs, that I can tell you," added Mama. "It will be a frame house. That is the mark of . . . what is the word? Progress. Getting ahead. The great step forward, next to clearing land and building a barn, of course, is crawling out of your log house into a new house made of lumber and siding and pretty paper on the walls inside."

"Just look at this," exclaimed Mama, suddenly discovering a crisply-spun cocoon clamped to a Juneberry twig. It was just what she needed to illustrate what was in her thinking.

"Someday it will leave this crowded little house

and fly out into a world of newness. So it is with the homestead family. Every woman dreams of getting out of her sagging log house into a house that stands tall and shiny along the country road. It's a great day when you move out of your old log house!"

Ingrid knew Mama was talking more to herself than to her. These were words that expressed the dream and hope in her heart. She wondered how long Mama would have to wait for this great transition. She had often heard Papa say, "It is not given to all of us to have much of this world's goods."

A few settlers were already building their frame houses, and several were making plans. Even Isaksons were drawing pencil sketches of a large, two-story house. Annie had shown Ingrid the plans one day. Ingrid had also seen some penciled lines on a paper in Mama's upper bureau drawer. Mama was secretly planning the room arrangement of her dream home. Ingrid was sure that the drawing of these sketches had in itself provided Mama with a certain degree of happiness.

"Then we will get a kitchen range like Mrs. South-of-town-Larson has, with that fancy, shining trim on the edges," mused Mama. "And a warming oven at the top, with two little shelves below it where the coffeepots stand when not in use. There will be a reservoir where water keeps warm, too." *Ja, ack,* to be able to move forward with the years! A kitchen range is every homestead woman's longing.

"We will have a well too." In the exciting fantasies Mama seemed completely oblivious to the fact that she was on her way to town. "Imagine what it would be like on a cold winter day to have a well and not have to go way out on the Big Lake and chop a hole in the thick ice. We would have a pump not far from the kitchen door, like Halvorsons in town have. All you do is work the handle up and down, up and down, until the water comes in a steady stream. Have you ever seen how they work?" Mama was finally aware of Ingrid's presence on the log beside her. *Ja,* Ingrid had seen how a pump works.

A frame house! A kitchen range! A deep well with a pump!

"But what about an organ, Mama?" Ingrid wished Mama had put that first on her list. She would be starting school in the fall and was old enough to become acquainted with this mysterious instrument that had the power to unlock the many feelings that lay crowded deep inside of her.

Ja, an organ. Ingrid should have an organ. She was sure she could learn to chord several songs.

"We will see," Mama answered, becoming suddenly aware that they were on the way to town. "This will never do. There is still the second stretch of the road untraveled. And then the Corduroy Road." Mama picked up her basket, and the game of pretending was over.

Feeling refreshed, they quickened their steps until they reached the end of the woods road. Stepping out of its tall shelter, they were face to face with the Corduroy Road. A straight, half-mile stretch lay between them and Town. But this April day the hostile forces were leashed, and the journey across the slough was pleasant enough.

There was much to be said for the Corduroy Road. Its course was interrupted in three places by rivers running lazily toward the sawmill. These waterways were spanned by rough plank bridges which bounced up and down pleasantly when you rode across them. The roadway itself was made of short cedar posts laid crosswise in washboard fashion. In the still of the night one could hear a wagon bumping across its ribbed surface for miles away.

Ja, the Corduroy Road with its open spaces on all sides! Papa called it the stern disciplinarian—*tukto-mästaren.* It could demand nine-tenths of the total strength expended in going to Town. Crossing it in the late autumn blasts, or in the winter blizzards, or the raw penetrating easterlies of spring, was something to remember always. Stepping from the windless seclusion of the woods into the openness of the Big Slough could be a shock to young and old.

"Set your face like a flint." That was one of Mama's oft-repeated proverbs. "Lift your shoulders high about your neck, pull your cap forward, and walk head first. Keep in mind the warmth of Klovstad's store—the big, red-hot stove, the lovely plants, the smell of coffee. Think only about the goal as you go through the storms. Up ahead is always some Klovstad's store."

* * *

Entering Klovstad's store was all a footsore traveler could wish, be it in the shiver of winter or in the heat of summer.

"Before we go to the counter let's look at Mrs. Klovstad's plants," suggested Mama, setting down the baskets on the floor.

The front windows of the store were flanked with cheerfulness—house plants of all descriptions and colors, all radiating a spirit of happiness and contentment. There were blossoms that resembled everything a child's imagination could conceive—bells, stars, umbrellas, blood-drops, slippers, ruffles, and all turning their smiling faces to greet the customers.

"Some of the soul of Mrs. Klovstad is in these plants," sighed Mama, giving them a fond, lingering look as she walked toward the counter with her eggs and butter.

"Well, *god dag,* Mrs. Hanson," greeted the storekeeper as he took Mama's baskets and began counting the eggs. "Fourteen to a dozen again, *ja, ack.*"

The round prints of butter wobbled on the counter as he set them down. Always a large extra pat was added to make the bottom of each print well-rounded instead of flat. They were pretty prints. As each pound came out of the round wooden mold in which it was packed, a lovely wild rose appeared on its face.

Klovstad added up the price of the products and then turned to Mama, knowing she would order groceries in exchange.

By this time Mrs. Klovstad put in her appearance. "So it is you, Mrs. Hanson. I thought I heard your voice. And Ingrid, too."

"Klovstad," she called softly to her husband, "be sure and fill a little bag of candy for the girl." Then she turned to Mama and whispered, "You come upstairs when you are done trading," and with a wink of the eye she returned to the stairway leading to their living quarters.

Klovstad's store was not big, and it contained a little of this and a little of that. There were mixed odors that greeted you as you came inside—salt herring, shoe leather, and harness—and across the back wall feed sacks were piled high. A large, red coffee mill stood on one counter, and whenever a pound of coffee beans was dumped into the large urn, the fragrance of Dr. Lyon's or Arbuckle's, whichever brand it happened to be, rose strong and fresh and friendly.

On the shelves along one wall of the store were bolts of calico, outing flannel, and black sateen. Beside it was a small showcase of alluring sweets. What tempting wonders! Chocolate jugs filled with cider, raspberry drops, shoe-lace licorice, creams and taffy twist, marbles and curlicues. And today Ingrid was asked to take her pick while Mr. Klovstad held a pretty, striped paper bag open and waited.

"Pick what you want most, now," he said. But shy Ingrid was afraid to choose. It all looked so good. There were lemon drops and peppermints, but she didn't care so much for these. But those chocolate jugs! If she could only dare choose those! She knew they were expensive, for Annie had bought some once. A penny apiece. She brushed her long, curly hair from her face and timidly said she would take some Rocky Mountain candy, since she didn't dare hesitate any longer. These were colored crystals, hard as stone, and clustered along a heavy string. You pulled these sweet morsels off the string with your teeth as you ate them. Ingrid received her bag of Rocky Mountain candy and started up the stairway to Klovstad's kitchen.

She could hear the clink of silver spoons and china as she climbed the stairs, and the smell of coffee greeted her warmly. Up here was the homestead customer's unfailing comfort. The storekeeper's wife was familiar with the affairs of the countryside, for circled around the glowing wood stove in the back of the store men settlers often sat warming their feet and tossing icicles from their beards on the red-hot iron lids. It was here each one exchanged his simple narrative of life, speaking a language learned in the hard school of experience. This was the common center where news was pooled and discussed. There were stories from logging camps and lumber mills, stories about land clearing, herds and crops, and new farm machinery. Here were reports of hardships as well as blessings, commentaries revealing the inner workings of these tillers of the soil as they sat relaxed, their feet resting on the iron rod surrounding the heater. Most of them had taken their conversations and stories with them, and they never hesitated to relate the same tale again and again. Occasionally a crystal of wisdom came through. Then they would nod assent in sober silence, and talking would cease for a moment or two.

And thus it was that the storekeeper's little wife, standing unnoticed behind the calico counter, listened well and remembered. And in the privacy of her own feminine circle around the coffee cups the women of the land learned of life about them. *Ja,* think.

Mama always felt refreshed and in high spirits when she picked up her basket of groceries and started for home. There was a new tug on life.

"*Ja,* women settlers need to get together just as much as the men," she told Ingrid as they walked the Corduroy Road from Town. "They need to know the heartbeat of the other women and how they grapple with life." Mama shifted her basket of groceries to the other arm. "Then you pick up your own bundle of life with new spirit."

Ingrid was sure that Mama had more than one thing in mind when she said, "I want to trade at Klovstad's, for there I can get a good cup of coffee."

4. Pastor Berg comes to the Shores

The settlement on the shores was not so desolate a spot any more—roads widening, fields expanding, crops and herds increasing, and new ideas creeping in.

But who could ever dream the day would come when the miracle of a modern machine for cutting hay would reach these parts? *Ja,* think! And who had not gone out to Gustaf Larson's farm to stand in silent awe beholding the great wonder with its rows of blades, and prongs, and joints, and arms—and Gustaf sitting like a king on the slender throne handling the maneuvers. Sparse as was his knowledge of the English language, he had not been slow in picking up a current expression that seemed pertinent at a time like this.

"Let her go, Gallagher," he called to his team of

horses, shaking the reins vigorously. And when the horses and the new machine moved through the field, long reams of hay fell to the ground like magic. *Jo-jomen,* that was something to see. Progress had set in without a doubt.

But to Papa Hanson it was not quite enough to feel the strain of the primeval yoke made easier. Were there not more important matters to be thinking of? The dream he carried in his heart was slow to ripen. He thought again of those few souls who had formed a congregation several years ago—what of their spiritual growth? their very life? How soon does man become involved with matters of the earth! The long months of winter had passed, and no servant of the Lord had visited these shores.

The only meeting we have had was the *julotta* at the Salbergs'," he reminded Isakson, as they walked the long way back from Gustaf's farm. "And now it is late spring."

"Now that the lake is open again and the boats have started to run, someone will be coming along." Isakson was hopeful enough.

"And what about our growing youth? How can their tender roots break through this dry ground?" Papa looked thoughtfully at the changes taking place all around. Progress could be both good and bad.

Then one fine day a letter came.

Dear Brother Hanson: Peace.

I have heard about you new settlers up there on Lake Superior. It appears now that I shall be able to visit your settlement sometime in June. If the Lord wills, I shall be in Ashland, Wis., around that time. Then I will try to come back by boat and get off at your dock. Till then, God bless you all.

Pastor Berg

Ja, now you can think the sun came out on the shores and there was reason for rejoicing. Pastor August Berg! Was it the personal magnetism of the man, or was it his great song and preaching? How little Papa had dared hope that such as he should light upon this humble settlement in the far wilderness. Could this be the beginning of a series of unfoldings leading to some fulfillment in the years to come? Papa had known the great preacher in his early days in America. It was in his temple that light had dawned and life had found new meaning—that Sunday evening in the years when Papa was an immigrant, lost and lonely.

"*Ja, du stora värld,*" said Isakson, when he heard the news. As soon as Papa had read the letter from Pastor Berg, he had leaped over the brush fence to tell his neighbor. Standing in the newly plowed field, they marvelled at the great occasion which awaited them. "Some time in June," he says—a robin rolled an arpeggio of praise from a nearby alder bush. Think, anyway!

So now you can believe the news got 'round. The great Minnesota preacher was to come! But no one knew the day. They had heard he had a love for rural places and often took excursions from his city pulpit to mingle with the tillers of the soil, be they white or black, or red with feathered heads. Log house, sod hut, wigwam—it made no difference. "Sometime in June," the letter said, but like all the unpredictables in life, one never knew the day, or the hour, this little man would light.

But the coming of a preacher had its problems, too. For then arose the old question which always loomed high in frontier women's hearts. "*Vem ska ta emot prästen?*" Glad they were to have a minister arrive, and blessed was the home which had the means and grace to offer hospitality. But, *ack!* Who could? Always the question, "Who shall take in the preacher?" *Ja,* say that. Shy and self-conscious as they were of their frugality and many limitations, it was no small matter to house a man of such degree.

To be sure, there were those who had time. Sofie Monson lived alone and had it cozy, but that would not be proper. Bachelors Guldstrand and Johnson in their humble shacks could never do it. Hammerstroms were much too far from town.

So it was up to Mama Hanson, Emma Isakson, and Lena Salberg to get their heads together and figure out a way.

"*Ja,* you, Lena, at least have a bedroom that can be closed off by your heavy draperies." It was Emma who had given thought to this. "And besides, you live in town where it is handy to the church. Then, too, you have no smell from barns and herds and swill pails, no chickens creeping close up to your door every minute of the day."

"And no flies!" added Mama, swishing her hands across her face. "To have city company with all these flies around, *ack,* what could be worse!" With a towel in her hand Mama batted a cloud of them toward the door and flung it open, frantically, for their escape.

"Give up the farm," said Lena, "and move away from barns and herds and sloughs and lakesides. Then you will be rid of them." Lena straightened in her chair, for she had more to say.

"You talk about smells and flies. But have you ever thought how lucky you are to have a root cellar full of potatoes and vegetables and eggs and such? And you," she said, nodding at Emma, "you have a spring house with pails of milk and cream standing in the ice cold water."

"*Ja,* but you can't put a preacher to sleep in the spring house, or even in the root cellar," answered Emma, a bit annoyed.

"*Ja,* talk never about that," said Mama, with a laugh ready to come through. "Neither can you put him in the kitchen when the family occupies the only other room. I was the one who put up Pastor Johnson from Duluth last fall," she reminded them. Mama rose to put some wood in the stove. "It wasn't easy, but that went too. Papa slept in the carpenter shed behind the house here, and the children and I laid on a straw mattress here in the kitchen. Pastor Johnson had the other room. It isn't easy when you know your company is used to nice city homes. But it goes." The fire was crackling briskly in the stove, and Mama hurried to set the tea kettle on the open flames.

"My, how glad I'll be when we get our frame house built," sighed Emma. "Don't forget I have had preachers in my log house too. Those first years when the family was smaller we could do it. But now we are six, and there comes a time when you must say *nej!*"

An awkward silence throbbed in the air, and Mama rose to lift the lid on the stove and put the coffeepot on. It was time to dispel the strange gloom that had settled.

"Well, I s'pose I can try to take Pastor Berg, since it seems to be up to me," said Lena, speaking with slow yielding.

"Oh, Lena, if you take him, with your bedroom

and all, Emma and I will pitch in and help you with the food problem." Mama looked for agreement in Emma's face. "Maybe Emma will bring in cream and eggs and–"

Jojomen, för all del–I will even kill a rooster and drag a slab of salt pork from the barrel." Emma was loud in her enthusiasm.

"And I will see that Papa brings you a sack of potatoes and rutabagas. I will even bake a molasses cake." With that Mama got up to put the coffee cups on the table. *Ja,* things were looking up now.

"You, Lena, have a way with people. You are guest-friendly and not so bashful as we backwoods women. I think Pastor Berg will like it at your house. It's an honor, Lena. What wouldn't Papa do to keep him here at our house! It is his sorrow right now."

Lena felt the warmth of a little praise, and the afternoon took on pleasantness as the coffee did its accustomed work of strengthening the spirits. There was comfort in knowing a great decision had been achieved. Pastor Berg would stay at Lena's house in town.

* * *

The budding countryside was settling into a peaceful Saturday evening when Pastor Berg arrived–overcoat, satchel, umbrella, and a leather Bible. Weary he was from the rolling trip across the lake, but with a smile for all that. A man of small stature, he had the smouldering fires of an artist in his eyes–an artist skilled in dealing with the human heart.

It was a warm handshake that he got from Papa Hanson, you can believe. "*Ja,* think, anyway, this is the Lord's doings, your coming here to us. How I have prayed that a messenger of God would come to us dried up souls. But never did I think it would be you, Pastor Berg. There must be some meaning in this."

Mama, though timid in the ways of receiving city folk, wasn't slow to poke up the fire in the cook stove. How tired Pastor Berg looked! *Ja,* traveling on a stormy lake was no rose-strewn path.

At the dock Pastor Berg had inquired his way to the Hanson homestead, then started off by foot along the sandy road. Little wonder he was tired, satchel and all.

"You must be starved as well as tired by now," said Mama timidly, as she served the great preacher a bowl of *välling* and beckoned Papa to sit down beside him at the table.

"*Ja,* you have right, Mrs. Hanson, it will be good to throw oneself full length in bed tonight. But do you have room for me here in your little log house?" Pastor Berg threw a swift look about the two-roomed cabin.

Papa explained that he would hitch up his horse and take Pastor Berg to the shoemaker's house in town, and added how sorry he was that they couldn't accommodate him here in their home. The great preacher understood.

Pastor Berg was well along on his second cup of coffee before Papa ventured to discuss Sunday plans with him.

Well, now, how shall we do it? It is necessary, you see, to get word around to the settlers, for they don't know you have come. We have no telephones so someone has to spread the news by way of mouth and foot. Sunday, that's tomorrow, you know."

"*Ja visst,* but it is too late to start out tonight. It is

best we wait until tomorrow to spread word. There will be but one service, and that will be in the evening. You have a long morning to get around."

Night had poured into the woods when Papa took Pastor Berg into town. Wonderful it was to ride through the quiet woods with the great preacher all to himself. The stars had blossomed out in full, and a pale moon came up over the pointed firs, making the forest all the denser. Here and there the white stem of a birch silvered by. Into the night's hush a dog barked from somewhere. "Likely Axel Olson's *hundvalp*" thought Papa, with no fondness for the creature.

There were so many things to talk about. Papa held the reins tightly lest the horse be tempted to take on speed. They spoke of homestead life, its limitations, the difficulties of a frontier congregation keeping the Spirit's flame alive. They discussed the times, the meaning of a prophetic Scripture verse. They recalled fond memories from their homeland, Sweden. They talked the language of the soul together. Pastor Berg called from his own depths to the kingdom within his brother's life, and Papa's hungering heart and mind found a satisfaction he had longed for all his life. For a brief hour he lived intensely and saw deeply. All human beings have an otherness. These soaring moments had a way of drawing out his best and highest self. *Ack*, if the road had been but twice as long! Starlight, moonlight, pine song, and matters of the soul. Greatness was in the night.

5. Spreading the Word

The first glow of dawn rose beyond the wooded hills, and there was a good Sunday feeling in the air. Papa was up with the first bird song and started off on horseback into the woods beyond the lake. In the upper woodland a lark poured out his heart in morning rapture. Papa was in exalted spirit. He had news that would add meaning to this day. No, it was not illness this time, nor death. It was life! A warm supply of Living Bread for those who would come to the little red church in town in the evening.

He turned off the main road into a thicket where a narrow path was concealed, forcing his horse through the bushes. It led to Bachelor Guldstrand's hut in Flag River Valley. But *ack!* Here was a footway meant only for the solitary wayfarer—slender, meager. The woods became full of frightened wings.

Bachelor Guldstrand had just gotten up and was making a fire in his stove when there came a knock at his door. Why, the sun had barely risen over the timber line, and here came a visitor. What in the big world could this mean?

Like all homestead bachelors, Guldstrand lived a special kind of existence. His one-room cabin was circled by dark wood. A patch of Sweet Williams bloomed under his window in the summertime, giving a touch of warmth. But in his little hut Guldstrand strummed his beloved guitar and sang the anthems of the soul till all the feathered song in sky and branch became an Eden rhapsody. There was heaven around Guldstrand's homestead when he sang.

"*Ja, men se* who's here," he exclaimed, opening the door to let Papa in. "As they say, '*Morgonstund har guld i mun'*; what brings you here, Hanson?"

"*Ja,* you said it," answered Papa. "The morning has gold in its mouth. I have good news."

Guldstrand pulled out his wooden rocker, waiting impatiently for the purpose of this morning call.

"*Nej, nej,* this is no time for rocking chairs," said Papa. "I have come to announce that Pastor Berg came last night and there will be a meeting tonight in the little red church in town."

"No, what say you! Pastor Berg! *Jaså,* he got here. We haven't had a church meeting since Pastor Johnson visited us last year."

"That you don't have to tell me," Papa said, drawing a sigh. "It's short notice, but try to come."

"*Ja visst.* I have a cow standing ready to calf, but it may hold off till I get back from the meeting. Now you must have a cup of coffee, Hanson, before you go further."

"*Nej, tack,* this is no time for coffee," and Papa turned toward the door.

"Now, Guldstrand," he said in gentle tones, "will

you give word to the other bachelors along the valley about the meeting? There is Hogberg, Ernst Johnson, Axel Johnson, John Olson. Maybe one of them can get to Hammerstroms with word. We want a goodly number out tonight. Now I must get up south of town to notify the Westlunds." Guldstrand promised to do his best, and with that Papa was on his way, bobbing up and down through the narrow trail. Guldstrand watched him go and shook his head.

"*Ja,* that Hanson, that Hanson. He doesn't stop for nothing."

Papa continued his journey, his face set townward. The Westlunds must be notified. There were two, three, other families along the road south of town, and no one knew if they were fish or fowl. But every human being has an ache and longing in his breast. He must call on them too.

Nearing town, he came upon Bachelor Broberg's clearing, neither round, nor square, but jutting in and out in leisurely disorder. *Ja,* Broberg. What should he do about Broberg? Should he stop or go right by? No, Broberg, too, had a soul.

Nearing the hut, he saw the lanky bachelor peeking through his only window like a woodchuck from his burrow. There were neither curtains in his window nor lock on his door. Like the woodchucks around him, he needed neither of these. Bachelor Broberg was a Swede of another feather. Quaint, good-natured, humorous of speech, and with the dialect of a "Dalmas," his ways and phrases lent themselves to ludicrous mimicry by young and old. He was an ardent lover of herbs, and on almost any pleasant morning he could be seen in woods or pasture gathering roots and wild plants to concoct into brews for ailments of various natures. For digestive disturbances he brewed a vile liquid from mountain ash berries. This was for those who had any kind of pain in the stomach. *"Ont i magen,"* as he said. Most folks were reluctant about experimenting with his potions, for, after all, Broberg was a queer one.

He had strange tales he loved to tell too, and these folks were not at all disinclined to listen to. One of his myterious experiences concerned a woman whom he claimed to encounter every now and then while walking along a certain path at night. Always they met in the same dark bend of the road. What they did or said was not revealed, but always she carried a coffeepot in her hand. *Nej, nej,* it was not imagination. It was real. Folks wondered if there was a secret mystery hidden deep in the bachelor's far-off past.

Broberg was a philosopher in his own way. He took great pains to set Papa Hanson straight on some biblical interpretations. *Ja visst,* he had a Bible in his hut, alright.

"Now you take the story of Daniel in the lions' den," he would say, brushing the old version aside with a fling of his long arm.

"You say it was a miracle that he was spared from the lions' teeth. Well, I can tell you how that happened. The lions didn't want him. Daniel had eaten too many vegetable greens. His flesh had no appeal to lions. Too many greens, that's what it was. *Grönsaker. Nej, du, lejonen ville inte ha han.*"

Papa didn't spend many minutes in Broberg's hut that day, though Broberg tried his friendly best to have him stay.

"Sit down, Hanson. Let's talk."

"*Nej,* this is no time for talk. You come to the meeting tonight and hear Pastor Berg."

"*Ja,* maybe that. But as far as a sermon goes I could tell Pastor Berg a few things myself."

Ja, Broberg was a queer one, but for all that, he had a busy head. Papa couldn't help but be amused at the strange orbit of his thinking.

"What a peculiar mixture of people we are up here in the backwoods where each man is free to think in his own way, with no one to bend, or shape, or direct, or enlarge one's thoughts," reflected Papa. There were those who found contentment in their limited existence and asked for nothing more. There were those too who hungered for more light, not satisfied to let their minds stand unused; then there were the few who knew their inner needs—the needs of the soul—and desperately reached out to find the Source of strength and spiritual renewal.

On the way back from the folks south of town Papa stopped at Widow Erickson's house to see how she was getting on, as he often did when passing. Here was another one with distinctions all her own. You knew a great deal about the character of this little woman the moment you stepped inside her friendly and neat little yard. Even as she shook your hand, you knew she was your friend.

The little garden in front of her humble home looked out upon the main road in town. It was a study of choicest pansies carefully tended. A few dandelions straggled along the edges, like poor relatives not welcome in the finer group. A clump of lilacs graced the entrance to her front door. Front doors, if there were any, were seldom used, and Papa knew it was a matter of great ceremony when she opened this door for him. Here on a table lay her Bible, edge-worn and faded, her silver-bowed glasses resting on the chosen morning psalm. In the window sill lay a pair of shears and a thimble.

Ja, old lady Erickson would come to the meeting, though by right she was a Lutheran. She would tell her Lutheran friends that August Berg was here.

It was mid-afternoon when Papa reached home, exhausted from his fling across the country. Mama saw how tired he was.

"Now when you have finished your dinner, you climb up in the attic room and get some rest; I will take care of the stable chores tonight and wake you in good time for the trip to church."

Papa started up the narrow stairs to the unfinished room under the eaves. What a haven was this undisturbed lodging with only the sound of the splashing waves below.

"If only a goodly number will come out tonight," he murmured, as he threw himself upon the homemade cot. His tiredness was of the pleasant sort, and he was not long in drifting off to sleep.

6. A SUNDAY EVENING

It was a Sunday evening made to be remembered, one to recall a thousand times when Junes return and pleasant reminiscences circle softly.

The stage was well set. For sound there was the symphony of frog song coming from the inlets of the Big Slough. Clover and wild cherry lent their fragrance. For scenery and lighting a sinking sun unfurled its diversity of coloring across the bosom of the Great Lake, sending its long fingers through the wooded land.

There was talk of a new way to church that Sunday evening. Neighbors as they were, about three miles from town, Isaksons and Hansons were going together, as was their usual custom. Papa had gone over to Isakson's stable with an idea in his head. An idea to do something out of the ordinary is not so dumb.

"My horse is tired after today's tramp, and your mule worked hard yesterday. What say you we take my boat and row to church?" Papa watched Isakson strip the milk cow dry and waited for an answer.

"The lake promises mild. What say you, Isakson, that we row?" he repeated.

"*Ja,* that I s'pose wouldn't be so dumb if your boat will hold us all. You are four, and we are six and a half since Emma is with child again."

Isakson rose and shifted his milk stool to the cow in the next stall.

"Are you sure the boat doesn't leak?" he asked, a little apprehensively.

"It isn't the first time a boat has leaked. We'll take a can and dip if necessary. As for room, the little ones don't take much space."

And so it was they pushed out from shore an hour later, right into the path of a dazzling sunset. A festive way of going to church, and different. It gave an awesome sensation, gliding away from land and the tall barricade of forest. Going to church was no small occasion at any time, but this night, with the lake hiding all its moods and tempers under a mask of sublimity, and a great man of God in the pulpit—how could it be anything but a night of wonder for old and young.

Papa took his place at the oarlocks, and Isakson settled down on the end seat, where water was prone to trickle in. The women and children huddled together on the remaining three seats.

Once out on the vast waters, it seemed like having left the world behind. A thrilling, expanded feeling came over the children as they watched the shore retreat. And there was not a lack of things to see.

"Sea gulls!" they shouted. "A tug!" "White sails!" "Stonequarry Point!" "A man walking on shore!"

The lake itself was in Sabbath preparedness. Tomorrow it might be in furious rage. No telling about this lake. It spoke in many languages, this fountain of water—the largest fresh-water body on the face of the globe. A sea gull searched and lamented, sometimes alone, sometimes a part of the flock. Sea gulls—forever soaring, circling, swooping over the deep.

"*Ack*, what scenes we have here on this lake," said Mama, coming back from far ports of thought. In her eyes was the look of one who has long sought horizons, who has stood in a doorway, or on a lonely shore, watching and waiting for a dark smudge to come out of the far-off dimness. The lake offers little that is seen at close range.

Isakson paused in his scooping and gazed across the water.

"I can't see what you folks find so wonderful about a lake and some sea gulls and a little boat. That's nothing."

"Oh, it isn't so much what we see as what we feel." Mama looked at Emma to see how she agreed.

"*Ja visst*, you have right. There is mystery here. I felt that the very first day we landed on these shores, soon eight years ago." Emma, too, had horizons in her eyes.

Ingrid and Annie found delight in running their fingers through the cool waters.

"This is more fun than taking the woods road to town," said Annie, Isakson's nine-year-old.

"Talk never about that," answered Mama, looking landward. "Just the same, the woods road is good to have when the northwest winds set in."

Tonight the familiar road to town lay silently tucked away in the tall timber back from shore. Tramped as it had been by many feet and wagon wheels, the ground had become soft with loose sand, unpleasant to the foot traveler with button shoes or low *tofflor*. But when the west wind was loose, then you can believe it was good to have the woods road.

Each stroke of the oars brought them closer to the mouth of the great harbor. Plask! went the oars cleaving the blue waters. Scoop! went the can dipping up the leakage. Over it all was the pleasant chatter of children's and women's voices. There was happiness out on the Great Lake.

"*Ja,* it will be good to hear a sermon again," remarked Isakson, addressing himself to Papa. "It don't seem we are making much headway with our handful of Mission Friends."

Papa had no immediate reply, but rowed for a moment in silence.

"No, it don't that," he said. "Our spiritual diet has been too lean. Our interest lies buried in our acres."

"Oh, there have been some high moments in the past," said Mama, overhearing the men. "You remember when Pastor Johnson from Duluth came last fall? Don't you recall how blessed we were and how his sermon moved our hearts? You remember how he sang about his childhood home in Sweden, his mother's faith and prayers—songs he had made up himself. There wasn't a dry eye when Johnson sang."

Pastor Johnson had struck some tender chords in the hearts of these new settlers. It left its benediction for many days to come. Springs of kindness entered human relationships, and while it lasted, they felt they were walking under an approving heaven. But as in all long stretches between pastoral visitations, the spiritual graces had worn thin.

"No, we are not where we should be," Papa said, resting his oars for a moment, "but there must come some answer to prayer up ahead. We may never see a large congregation or a church with a steeple pointing to the sky. It don't look that way. But there may be seeds that will come to harvest in generations beyond our own. We must build spires in the hearts of our young if we don't build them any other place."

They reached the yawning mouth of the harbor and turned their boat cautiously into the solemn aisle of water. Sea gulls, poised on the wave-splashed piers, stood guard on either side. There's a special feeling in entering a harbor with its silent depth, a mixture of fear, exaltation, and security all in one, thought Papa, as he drew a deep breath.

"A harbor is a great accomplishment," he said, stroking the waters with grave respect. "A mark of progress. Yes, sir."

"*Ja,* say that. We have paid for this canal with our own hands," remarked Isakson. "I remember how we dug and slaved. It isn't deep for nothing."

Reaching the dock, they tied their boat to a pier and hoped for a dry landing. A stairway led to the high tramway where piles of freshly-sawed lumber rose high on each side.

Jojomen, here we have the fruit of our winter's labor in the logging camp." Isakson paused to size up the tall monuments, boards piled crisscross in layers against the sky. "Soon the lumber boats will come and carry these millions of boards to where they build cities, and there ends the story of our labor in the timberland. Cities."

From the high tramway there was still a half-mile left to the corner of town where the red church stood.

"Here we have the Great Lake behind us, the Big Slough under us, and town in front," said Emma, straightening her plump figure as best she could. Somehow the new way to town belonged to the June evening—the lake way, the harbor way, the tramway and church.

"It seems changing one's way of doing things, now and then, isn't so dumb. 'A change makes new,'" quoted Papa, trying to translate a Swedish proverb. "Stick to your Swedish, man," suggested Mama. "'*Ombyte förnöjer.*' That's what you mean."

They passed the silent sawmill and entered town. The peace of the evening lay beautiful over the scattered dwellings as they followed the main street toward the road which led to the church. Here and there a cowbell clanged from squares of pasture land between houses.

The soft glow of a sun well set still clung to the windowpanes of the little church as they drew near. How simple was this building, standing in a weed-grown edge of town. But for one thing it could have been taken for a community hall, or a shop, or even a barn. During the building of this plain structure someone with an eye for the sanctity of God's house had seen to it that the three windows which graced each of the two long walls were fashioned as artfully as possible and with the reverence becoming the temple of God. The windows, long and narrow, rose to a spired top, a triangle, where three glass panes were fitted together, one red, one white, and one blue, a thoughtful, but crude, attempt at a stained-glass window effect.

"Do you suppose the time will come when we will have a church of our own?" whispered Emma, when she and Mama were well settled on the plain board benches of the sanctuary, each with a little one on her lap.

Mama looked wistfully into Emma's face. "*Ja,* say that. It is good we can meet in this building that the handful of Presbyterians got together and built."

"*Ja,* the Presbyterians—what has become of them? They don't have meetings any oftener than we," said Emma.

"That you can well see," agreed Mama, looking about the room. Cobwebs of various patterns hung in the ceiling and curtained the corners of the window frames. The long periods when the double doors remained closed had left a mustiness in the air. Mama sighed deeply. "*Ja,* they too began with high hopes, but it didn't last. *Ack,* there is something so sad and lonely about a country church standing at a barren edge of town with neither lights nor song."

It was beginning to get dark when the last wagon rolled up beside the church. From it stepped Hammerstrom and Lotta and even Sofie Monson from the hills. Papa stepped up on a chair and began lighting the three kerosene lamps suspended from the ceiling.

Little Ingrid Hanson had begged to sit next to the open window overlooking the town and the Great Lake below. There would be music tonight, and she knew it would be doubly meaningful if she could look out upon the night, upon the thread of lights across the wide waters. The old reed organ, the only luxury the church had stored within its walls, had been given to the Presbyterians by a well-to-do city man. Now it stood on the platform, waiting for the touch of a familiar hand. Ingrid longed for that moment. She had attended meetings here before. She knew what that organ did for her. Ever since her young heart had discovered its beauty, its soul, she had begun a dream. She had decided desperately that some day she, too, would draw heavenly melodies from an organ.

Turning to her mother, she whispered, "Do you think we can buy an organ some day?"

"*Ack*, that will be the day, Ingrid. But who knows. More impossible things have happened. You are young yet. When the time comes, there will be a way." Mama, too, longed for an organ. It should not be too hard to learn to chord, she thought. *Ja,* think—a reed organ.

7. THE CADENCE OF A SONG

Three closing words—the cadence of a song carried on wings unseen into the heart, into the night, into the stream of time. Could this hold the power to return a thousand times, to live forever, to cause one to listen for the things which have never been spoken? The cadence of a song. What a little thing to remember when much else is forgotten, to embrace for a lifetime, to recall with tears.

The great Sunday evening service was about to begin. Papa Hanson's prayers had been rewarded. A large group of settlers had come out, old and young. Lutherans and Mission Friends and others who had no denominational name. Each was seeking something new and refreshing, something to fill the emptiness of the soul. A row of lanterns stood friendly-like along the back wall of the sanctuary, and the odors of barns and new-turned soil rose strong about the room.

There fell a hush upon the congregation when Pastor Berg took his place on the low platform. He faced his audience with the dignity that becomes a minister of the Word. There was gentleness in his voice when he bade them welcome and announced the number of the first hymn. The congregation rose to sing, but there was weakness and tightness in the singing.

"Sing out!" called Pastor Berg. "Open your mouths and hearts wide and sing! Alright, let's try it again. *Sjung!*"

The backwood shyness, which held them bound and unsure, began to loosen with each verse of the song, but it was not until the third song that they found it in them to really sing. It was the song about a human sigh, stealing unheard, like a dove, toward heaven. The evening began to swell. Voices of many qualities and dialects flowed into the rural night. Frontier people, wrestling with hardship, poverty, and sorrow, having once opened the floodgates of the soul, sing as none other. Adversity adds a richness of feeling to the human voice.

"Wonderful!" called Pastor Berg. His own abundant voice rose above the others, and soon the few who felt that singing was not for them began to take courage and joined with the rest. Like a wave growing fuller and larger on its swell toward shore, the song surged and lifted until it seemed as if the very roof could hold it down no longer, as if the deep yearning of mankind pierced every barrier between heaven and earth.

Fram en suck sig smyger,
Hörd av ingen vän,
Dock lik duvan flyger
Den mot himmelen.

Pastor Berg knew he had selected the right song. He understood the hearts of these simple folk. A joyous song did not sing so well. They were not a lighthearted people. Their inclinations drew toward the minor mood—solemn, yet tender and moving. With tear-filled eyes they sang, looked up, and hoped again.

Soon came time for the sermon. Pastor Berg had his material gathered. All that was needed was to set it aflame with the Spirit of God. Not so much a man of letters, Pastor Berg possessed a certain eloquence that appealed to every mind and soul. He knew the artful ways into the heart of man. He, himself, had lived, erred, bled, and come forth the stronger. He knew the grace of God. And though he spoke with stern conviction on the subject of sin, emphasizing the truth with thunderous voice and sharp fist-blows on the pulpit, in the next moment tears of tenderness came through, and his voice gentled as he entered the realm of God's love and mercy.

"O my friends," he said in softer voice, "we find God in the shining stars and in the flowers by the roadside, but in the ways of men we find Him least of all. It ought not so to be."

And in this June evening of the late '90s he spoke once more about the grace of God—*Gud's nåd.* How often in their weakness had they embraced that word —*nåd.* Pastor Berg did not hide his observations of these human folk. He called attention to indifference and lack of warm cooperation. He warned them of the Adam in man's nature.

And in the cool of the evening each listener heard the call—"Where art thou?" Where would they be but for the grace of God? Who could not point to some dark corner in his life that night? But there was the promise, made new again, spoken by the great prophet, the poet Isaiah. Pastor Berg's kind voice rose full as he assured them—"Though your sins be as scarlet, they shall be as white as snow." When the sermon was ended, horizons had been enlarged.

It was then they sang the closing hymn, the hymn which helped them feel anew God's handclasp. Each stanza ended with the three undying words, "Saved by grace"—*frälst av nåd.*

Pastor Berg paused in his own singing to study the faces of his singing congregation and considered the diversity of human nature to be found among these people. Yet now they sang as one in beautiful agreement. They sang from hearts which felt a common need. They knew their sinfulness.

"Oh, that they might hold this moment long," he prayed within himself. "Next time," he planned, "my subject shall be victory. God's grace they seem to understand, but victory—that's a new chapter."

"Saved by grace." In his study of the audience that night Pastor Berg had missed the little girl sitting by the open window. Eight-year-old Ingrid could almost see the tone-clothed words rise and flow into the night. She listened with more than the ears of a child to the long sweeping notes, so pure and sublime yet holding a certain sadness in their length. Perhaps it was that strange wistfulness that gave the refrain its beauty. A pioneer child grows older than her years. There was more than words and music in what she heard that night. She found her heart straining to catch a faint sound that had the nature of a call in it. Thoughts she had never known before surged through her young mind, thoughts too formless yet for words, feelings she could not quite piece together.

"Saved by grace." She knew the word "grace" held wonder, for she had often heard it spoken by the older folks. And when Papa sang his favorite song, "God's grace is new each morning," his face lit up and tears shone in his eyes. *Nåd!* It must be God's choicest gift to man, something warm, forgiving, the thing to cling to in life, the desperately needed anchorage in death. Through the mists of early youth she was beginning to understand a little.

Three long words—a cadence with a high tone, then a low, both struggling for a mooring in the closing note, which was neither high nor low but a restful haven in between the two. Grace—the last word to taper off into the dark immensity of night.

The cadence of a song. A child looked out into the evening, now rounded out by darkness. It was not the lean pattern of the village lights that she saw. It was not the dark spread of the Great Lake below, nor the towering forest. Her world had suddenly grown large. The awe of saluting what comes from a higher world is a divine experience!

8. Getting Ready for the Conference

Slowly the year turned from winter to spring, and then came May. By now the wilderness was alive with chitterings and flutterings, chirrs, kweets, and caws. And to heighten the glory there came a letter to the shores.

"*Jojomen,*" said Isakson, coming into Mama's kitchen one afternoon with fresh mail from town, "a letter to Hanson from Duluth." He handed Mama the letter along with the Minneapolis *Veckoblad.*

"I should just wonder what can be in that letter," Isakson asked, not so little curious. But Mama, preoccupied with *Veckobladet,* laid the letter aside, and Isakson started back, asking no more questions.

"Oh, my, excuse me," called Mama, coming to herself. "Many, many thanks for the mail."

"Var så god," answered Isakson, waving the matter aside, a little disappointed.

Veckobladet. That was something to get in the wilderness. It contained a continued story—*följetång*—by an author named Leonard Strömberg, and Mama looked forward eagerly to Tuesdays! Then someone on the shores would go to town and bring back the mail. And always in the post would be the Swedish weekly with this fascinating serial. It was the bright spot in her week. Each chapter ended on an exciting note that filled the following seven days with pleasant anticipation of what was to come next.

Mama glanced at the clock and saw that it was three-thirty and time to bring coffee to the field, where Papa and the horse were pulling stumps. There was no time to read the *följetång* now. She would save the warm moment for the evening hour when work was done. It would be pleasant then when all was quiet. Besides, she was curious herself about this letter. Letters were no ordinary events on the shore. She hurriedly packed her basket and set off for the field, the letter in her apron pocket.

Papa saw her coming and led the horse to the patch of grass at the edge of the clearing. Nearby a fallen maple tree provided a good bench on which to sit while the chime of cups and saucers and the aroma of coffee filled the atmosphere. Never did coffee taste so good!

"But what have you there?" asked Papa, as his gaze fell on the letter poking up from Mama's pocket.

"Ja, it came in the mail Isakson brought from town. But finish your coffee, and then you can read it loud."

Papa gulped down his coffee and hastily tore open the letter

"Can you think, it comes from Pastor Johnson of the Mission Church on Second Street! *Ja,* think anyway." Papa began reading:

> Dear Hanson:
>
> There is going to be a Bible Conference in our church in June the 15th to the 18th. It would be good if someone from the south shores could join us, particularly yourself, who worked here so faithfully in past years before you became a homesteader. We hope you can find it possible to come.
>
> Your faithful servant,
> John J. Johnson

A conference in the church on Second Street, in the city which shone like a silver thread across the Great Lake when night fell on! That was going to be something. And important it was that Hanson, himself, come. It was in this church that he had met Mama after coming from Sweden. It was here they were married. In this church Mama had sung in the choir when as a hired girl she got her Sunday evenings off. Here Papa worked as a deacon and gave unstintingly of time and substance. *Ja, ack,* it would feel good to be back again.

But Mama, too, might like to go. They couldn't both go, however, for it would cost too much for boat fares. And besides someone must stay home and see after the cows.

"You are the one to go," said Mama, with finality. "We will manage here on the shores. We can press up your wedding suit, and the old Swedish satchel under the rafters is always ready for use. Perhaps Augusta can come down from Duluth and spend a week with me. She wrote she was quitting her place anyhow. She didn't like her lady." Mama gathered her coffee things in the basket and started back to the house.

"*Ja, ack, ack,* if I could only get to the conference," said Papa, half aloud, to himself and the horse, as he resumed his task among the stumps. It's the time of year that's bad—seed time, cultivating, and fences to put up. But it was also important that time be given to the nourishing of the soul. Man needs food for the inner life. The winter, as always, had left its spiritual barrenness. The work of the little congregation was almost at a standstill. Perhaps if he went to the conference, he would come back with fresh inspiration and a bit of the glow which Moses carried from Mount Sinai. *Ja,* he would go. Come what may, he must be at the conference.

So now things began to bustle down by the shores. It was Mama who conceived the idea of having Ingrid accompany Papa to the Big City. She had never seen a city, only the lights across the lake. It would do her good to see the world, to get out among city folk and see how they conduct themselves. Then, too, she would have a chance to hear great music. *Ja,* of course, Ingrid must go with Papa. All she really needed was a new dress. Her coat wasn't too bad. Mama did some close figuring. A dress—*ja,* there would be a way.

Over at the neighbor's house there was excitement too. If Papa was going to the conference, why couldn't Emma use this opportunity to go and visit her relations, the Pilstroms, who lived in the Big City? Now she would have help on the journey. Emma had a little one again, Ernst, born on the last Fourth of July, a patriotic one for sure. She would have to take him and one other child. Isakson could manage with the other two in the worst case.

"I think we ask Sofie Monson to come down for a few days," suggested Isakson, in discussing Emma's trip with her one evening. "She could take care of the house and children while I am in the field. No doubt the change will do her good, sitting as she does all alone on her claim."

So that was that. Emma was to go to Duluth, too. She wondered which one of the children to take along besides baby Ernst. It was soon settled when Ingrid came rushing breathlessly into their cabin.

"I'm going to Duluth!" she shouted, even before she reached the lilac clumps outside their kitchen door. Ingrid's world had suddenly been heightened, and transformed. Never had the clouds above seemed so friendly. Never had a bird in flight been so meaningful. Everything about her smiled. She was setting out for places where her young spirit had often flown in rare moments of fantasy. She was going to see what lay beyond that mysterious thread of light which shone across the vast lake in the hush of night.

When Emma saw the glow on Ingrid's face, she decided which one of her children she would take along. She would take Annie.

Annie! Ingrid's cup was running over. She rushed over to Annie. They clasped arms tightly and jumped up and down till the log cabin floor bounced with joy too. Everyone's heart was beating fast these days.

And from Augusta came a letter. *Ja,* she would come and stay with Mama while Papa and Ingrid were at the conference. *Ja,* she would bring two and one-half yards of blue cotton serge for a dress for Ingrid. *Ja visst,* she would come a day early so she and Mama could sew up the dress in time for the trip. Oh, it would be fun, the two women alone over there.

And Sofie Monson was not so little glad to come away from her home in the hills to be with Isaksons so Emma could get away for a visit with her relatives as well as enjoy the fruits of the conference. Everything worked smoothly on the shores. To Annie and Ingrid there had never been a May like it. Life was full.

"Don't be too over-happy," warned Mama, when Ingrid bubbled over with exclamations. Ingrid wondered why Mama always said that when someone was in seventh heaven. Could it be something she had learned in girlhood, back in Sweden? *Var inte för glad, du.*" In her warning she seemed to imply that, like as not, one extreme of mood could quickly follow on the heels of the opposite.

But for Emma there came to be some wrinkles in the cloth. She entered Mama's cabin one morning, and the happiness Mama expected to see was not there.

"What is the trouble, Emma? With all the excitement ahead you should be singing like that meadow lark out there." Mama pointed to the window facing the field. But, *ack,* Mama knew that happiness was not without flies in the ointment.

"Well, the thing is this," said Emma, settling herself on the kitchen chair. "Now that the way is open for me to go to Duluth, I got to thinking about my clothes. You know, Betty, we've scarcely had a new rag since we came to sit on our homesteads."

Mama nodded, her lips firmly pressed. She knew what Emma meant. She had been thinking about

Emma's wardrobe during the night. True, the Isaksons were making more progress than the Hansons. While there would be two boat fares to pay, now that Annie was past seven, that would not be too great a problem. But when it came to clothes, that was another chapter. Emma didn't have time to sew, and to buy anything in the little backwoods town was impossible.

"Let me think a minute," said Mama, stroking back her brown hair. To go to the stylish city people with old, faded clothes, threadbare and wrinkled, that was no fun. "*Nej*, then I think to stay home," said Emma. She needed a dress, a hat, and a wrap of some kind. And her shoes didn't look so good, either, with tramping the brush and the deep sands.

"That summer cape of mine, isn't it a little blacker than yours?" asked Mama.

"Oh, my yes. Mine has turned gray from fade."

"You take my cape then. That's that." Mama turned her thoughts to Emma's other garments.

"Now I tell you what we'll do. We'll get together and rip up your black skirt, turn it inside out, and it will be like new. Then your hat. Tear off the old pansies on your sailor, and you can sew on the red roses Augusta gave me. She got them from the lady she worked for. They're not bad. Now if the men will half-sole your shoes, we can trim the loose threads from the brocaded tops, and there you are, stylish as a peacock. You can wear your half gloves. They can't be too out of style." Mama looked at Emma and saw that the weather in her face had changed.

"*Ja*, you are the sun on a cloudy day, Betty," said Emma, rising to go. "Now I feel better."

"*Ja*, we must always talk our troubles over together. Two heads are better than one. You know, Emma, I, too, will go to Duluth some day. Then I shall need to borrow things from you. So we have always stood together, you and me."

There was a tear coming through in Emma's eye when she left Mama's kitchen. When she reached the first turn in the path, she looked back, and there was Mama standing in the doorway. They waved goodbye to each other in an understanding way.

There was much astir on the shores those days in May. Papa ploughed and seeded and fenced from dawn to dusk. The days were too short at that. During the night he would wake up and think about the conference. He would have to bring greetings from the Mission Friends on the south shore. *Ja,* what could he say? *Ja,* say that.

As for Mama, she sewed and pressed and cleaned and patched. And soon it was the day when Augusta was to come.

The big steamer, *Hunter,* would arrive most any hour that Friday afternoon, one never knew just when. Likely enough Augusta would be on it, for the next day the people on the shores must leave for the conference. Once having deposited her at the dock, *Hunter* would follow the south shore to Bayfield and then to Ashland, stopping here and there at smaller ports along the way. On its return the next day the steamer would pick up the conference delegates and whatever freight and luggage that awaited its return.

It was a wonderful feeling to wake up on the day Augusta was to arrive. Augusta, with all her laughter and funny capers. How torn Ingrid felt about leaving, now that her aunt was coming. Of all times not to be home! But the trip to the Big City, and especially with Annie, was too rare to miss.

"You must run down to the shore right often now," said Mama. "It is past noon, and *Hunter* can show up most any time. A speck on the horizon could be it. That gives Papa time enough to hitch up and get to the dock to meet Augusta. Be sure to keep a steady eye on the lake."

It gives one a strange excitement, waiting for something to appear on the line where sky and water meet. "It might be it," you say. "It might be it." Hope flutters a bit, and then you see it. Out on the rim is something dark. The coming of a big steamer is a high experience—first the dot, tiny and black, hidden in a puff of smoke. Then it grows in size, and soon it has changed to white, ever growing in bulk until its brow points right at the one standing on shore—waiting, watching, hoping. It is a time of wonder when the big horn on the topmost deck begins to blow. Then it blows again, and still again, as if to say, "I mean it!" Three times it blows, and the last call is long and final.

More than once had Annie and Ingrid walked the sandy miles, barefooted, to stand on the dock when the great ship entered port. That which had been but a dot a half-hour before was now an immense, luminous cliff, its walls towering and glittering as it advanced slowly into the harbor. Here was the story of might and strength and a hundred storms! Here was magnificence!

This day Ingrid saw *Hunter* in even greater glory as he moved with solemn dignity into the harbor, the sudsy waters eddying softly at his sides. Again came that pleasant ache of wonder welling up inside. Life was on a swell.

On the lower deck black figures soon became passengers moving about. Right at the point of the deck someone was waving a head scarf for all she was worth. It was Augusta.

At home Mama waited and listened for the squeak of wagon wheels. But she needn't have listened for wagon wheels, for within a mile of their destination Augusta's laughter ran on ahead of them. It rang through the woods in long vibrations of merriment. Papa didn't say much. Augusta did the talking and laughing very sufficiently by herself! This woman beside him on the seat was a strange one.

Mama saw them come out of the woods into the open space in front of the log house. Augusta had come, satchel, bundles, paper bags and all.

"Have you got a cup of coffee ready, Betty?" she called, even before she stepped down from the wagon.

Ingrid couldn't wait to see the oranges and bananas which she guessed were in the paper bags. She was anxious to see the blue cotton serge which was to be transformed into a dress before another day dawned.

That evening, when they were washing the supper dishes, Augusta related her latest episode as a hired girl in the home where she served.

"Can you believe, I was dusting the furniture in the nice parlor, and when I came to the piano, temptation got the best of me. I did so want to try my fingers on those keys. I was sure my lady had gone out, the house was as still as a graveyard. So I tried to finger out a melody from Sweden. *"Du gamla, du fria, du fjällhöga nord.*" It took time, but I got so far I could play the first line in the song with one finger. *Ack*, it was beautiful. Then I played louder and louder, and what do you s'pose? Out from some corner came steps that shook the whole house. Mrs. Edmond had not gone out."

"Augusta," she yelled. "I thought I had explained to you a servant girl's place in this house. You are here to clean and dust and not take the privileges of a family member." "Alright, I quit," said I, and that was that. I went right upstairs to my attic room and packed my satchel. I knew I was welcome to stay with my friend Tekla in West End."

Ja, Augusta was independent, a Swede of another color. She had skin on her nose, alright. And a mouth she had, too.

It was late that night before Mama and Augusta got at the sewing of Ingrid's dress. Papa went up to the little room in the attic to sleep with Anders. Ingrid went to rest on the sofa in the big front room, which was parlor and bedroom combined. If there was anything left of the night after the dress was finished, Augusta and Mama would sleep in the big bed in the same room.

That night there was little sleep on the shores. Ingrid couldn't forget the next day. The tomorrow can have a powerful grip on the night's sleep. Several times she awakened to see the two women across the room huddled close around the kerosene lamp on the machine. They talked in low voices, reviewing the shadows which had crossed their paths since last they met. Ingrid couldn't hear everything, but there were a lot of "*ack, acks*" and "*kära hjärtans.*" Out in the kitchen the fire crackled in the wood stove, and the smell of coffee was pleasant about the place. Things were cozy, and the low drone of voices soon lulled her to sleep again. Each time she awakened, the scene was the same, there was the same crackling in the stove, the same fragrance of coffee. Once she peeked through the window beside the sofa and was sure she saw a yellow light through the woods coming from the Isakson window. Maybe Emma was up too. She wondered if Annie could sleep. Maybe they were sewing over there, too, with fires sputtering and coffee cooking on the stove. It was a wonderful night.

The waves splashed sleepily on shore, and there were night songs in the upper branches of the pines. At last, with all this peace around her, Ingrid fell into her last stretch of sleep.

When she awakened the next day, there was much ado out in the kitchen. Milk pails, calf pails, pans, kettles, and dishes were all in an argumentative clatter, and the emphasis was that there was no time to lose, though the sun was not over the east woodland yet.

"Up now, Ingrid. *Morgonstund har guld i mun.*" Mama's call had its usual proverb.

This was the big day. Papa yawned at the breakfast table. Augusta rubbed her eyes. Mama dragged her feet wearily. Ingrid couldn't quite clear her thinking as to all this day involved. Across the rocking chair in the living room hung her new dress, blue cotton serge.

"Who is going to take you to the dock today?" asked Augusta, pouring out a cup of coffee.

"Oh, that will Isakson do," answered Papa, shoving

his chair from the table. "But as the day wears on, now, we must all keep an eye on the lake. When *Hunter* comes around the Big Ravine point, we must hurry to be off."

"There's something about the lake this morning that tells me we are in for strange weather," said Mama, a little cloud of anxiety in her voice. Mama's sensitivity to oncoming weather disturbances was more than ordinary intuition. She had become acquainted with certain winds, certain skies, certain colorings on the lake, a special kind of stillness in the woods. When she saw a familiar cloud rise in the west, there was no time to lose. Off for the root cellar they would go without any "*om*" or "*men.*" But not Papa. He was never afraid of storms. He would keep right on ploughing, or pulling stumps, storm or no storm. When the tempest was over and Mama and the children emerged from the root cellar shelter, Papa would wave at them from the field. Mama pretended not to see.

It was noon when Ingrid detected a smudge rising over the gray waters by the Big Ravine bend. Then there was some scrambling, and in no time, it seemed, Isakson's wagon was full of passengers. Mama walked over to her neighbors to see them off. Sofie Monson, too, was there. She drew up close to Mama to tell her how glad she was Augusta had come. What a time the three women would have!

"*Ja,* Emma, you look so stylish, as nice as the fine lady on this year's calendar," said Mama, picking a loose thread off Emma's borrowed cape. "You can hold your head as high as the next one. And the red roses in your sailor hat give color to your face. *Ja,* you don't need to take any back seat for nobody."

Emma looked pleased and made herself comfortable on the wagon seat.

"*Ja,* good-bye with you now," she said, waving a half-gloved hand at Mama.

There were other good-byes and wavings, and the old mule team started them on the first move toward the great conference.

9. The storm

There was something ominous about that afternoon. The weather seemed to be holding something back that it might suddenly let loose. Standing beside the listless waves, two miles up the shore from the dock, Mama recognized the familiar pattern. She felt a sense of uneasiness as she thought of the ones who were about to set out on the unpredictable waters. Looking toward the west, her hand shielding her eyes, she could see the big steamer back out from the harbor and set its prow for the middle lane of the immense lake.

Out on the steamer's broad deck two wide-eyed girls—Annie and Ingrid—watched the ever-widening gulf of water separate them from the familiar coastline. This was a special sensation they had never experienced before. Oh, they had pushed out from shore in a rowboat many times, but this was different —a beyondness, awesome and throbbing. Seen from the boat, the green clearings were soon absorbed by the darker green of the forest. In no time the log cabins melted into the walls of timber and were lost to the eye. The only recognizable landmark was Stonequarry Point, protruding halfway out to the steamer. And in no time this, too, would be a thing of the past. They were being transported into a new world.

Out on the water's depths *Hunter* turned his huge hulk halfway around and started westward with determination. The sound of ripping waters reminded Ingrid of bedsheets being torn in two.

In the large passenger room people were seated along the walls, most of them studying each other in mute, bashful silence. Here were homesteaders, villagers, a few city folk, all picked up at ports along the south coast of the lake, many of them Swedish, Norwegian, and Finnish. Children were seated on chairs beside their parents, content for a time just to absorb with their eyes and ears all that this strange adventure had to offer. The hissing waters spoke of speed, time, and miles uninterrupted.

And then the sky darkened. Suddenly a violent wind began to ruffle the vast prairie of water.

"Look at that ugly cloud!" shouted Annie, pointing to the west.

Ingrid recognized the cloud. It was the same funnel-shaped enemy which Mama feared so often. She called it "sickloon." Whenever she sighted its appearance, there was no time to lose. Everything alive, except Papa, had to follow her, instantly, to the root cellar behind the house. But out here on the open sea there was no root cellar within reach. What would they do if this should turn into a "sickloon"?

Annie and Ingrid hurried into the passenger lounge,

and it was plain to be seen that here was uneasiness and strain. Even the men pacing the deck looked helplessly at each other with a silent shake of the head. Darkness deepened in the sky, and sharp bolts of thunder and lightning ripped the air.

Papa rushed in from the windy deck and saw a seasick look on Emma's face as she rocked unsteadily on her chair, baby Ernst in her arms.

"*Men kära hjärtans,* what is this going to turn into?" she asked, with anxiety in her voice.

"Oh, this will blow over," Papa consoled her. "Likely just a June sqall. If it were fall, it would be a different story. Then we know Lake Superior can become as bad as the great 'Atlanten' itself. But not so likely in June. *Nej, du.*" But Papa was never afraid of storms.

Everyone knew what treacherous tempests could blow up during the fall months, particularly November, sometimes lasting for several days. Had not the folks along the shores seen and heard their terror? Had they not gone down on the sandy beach and found endless wreckage strewn about—barrels, boxes, lumber, and logs? Even orange and banana peelings washed up amid the froth of the waves lay temptingly on shore. Many a morning after a storm Mama would be seen on the driftwooded shores examining the night's deposit, always expecting to discover some rare treasure tucked in amid the debris. "Someday I'll find it," she would prophesy. "Someday."

But this was no ordinary squall that met the folks aboard the *Hunter* bound for the conference. Over on the horizon a line darkened and widened as it approached in the form of an enormous fold of green water. Swiftly behind it came another and another. The large steamer began to lift, and sway, and creak, and writhe. The furniture danced and rolled across the decks. Passengers' faces paled from fright and seasickness. *Ja, ack.* Would that they were on land again! How unreachable were those wooded shores in the distance!

A fiercely dark hour passed. And then, as if some unseen power had commanded "Peace, be still," the winds began to subdue, the clouds scattered, and almost apologetically the waves lowered and crouched along the foot of the big ship. A long, deep sigh of relief swept across the vast waters. The storm was resolving into peace, and a deep anxiety was lifted from the heart of every passenger.

When at last everything was restored to order, the steamer resumed its journey toward the Big City. In the passenger room conversation was free and uninhibited. Now they were one in a real way. *Ja,* I should say so. Had they not shared a dark moment together? Had they not been spared from what might have been a great peril? Now they drew close to each other in a warm, relaxing manner.

"No, Lake Superior isn't nothing to fool with," said an old Norwegian fisherman, shaking his head as he filled his corncob pipe. Soon other pipes were drawn from hip pockets, and the air became pungent with the odor of La Turka tobacco.

"*Ja,* you have right," agreed a Finnish settler from up the lake. "Superior is a queer one." From his mackinaw pocket he took out a bag of peppermints and passed around the circle. There was a good feeling on board.

Papa couldn't resist humming a song that was traveling through his mind. It was a Swedish hymn about journeys over rough seas with distant harbor lights in view. Emma knew the song, and little by little she was joining him. Hadn't they sung it together many times in their early pioneer days? Presently others on board were singing too. It came easy to learn the words of the refrain. They knew the meaning now.

Uti storm vi stå
Snart vi sälla hamnen nå . . .

While soft waves of song filled the air, the sun appeared through the broken clouds, and the oncoming evening was like a beautiful vesper.

"What a lovely way to end the stormy chapter," said Emma, as her eyes swept across the reverent stillness of the room.

"Oh, come quick, Annie!" called Ingrid, opening the door to the deck. In the distance tall, gray hills loomed magnificently against the sunset sky. Little dots of houses wedged in among the ledges of the hills resembled dishes in a china closet. Tall shafts of smoke rose from larger buildings huddled close to the foot of the hill. There was the Big City—Duluth! It was no more a thread of light, a dream, a fantasy. It was real!

"*Ja*, think anyway," said Papa, with awe in his voice. "Here we have a city almost thirty miles long, one mile high, and one mile wide." He had tramped this strange strip of town from end to end in his earlier years in America. "No, sir, Duluth is no ordinary city."

Dusk began to settle, and twinkling lights set like jewels in the misty hills extended a welcome as they drew near. On both sides of the great harbor tall pillars capped with streaming lights guided the storm-weary steamer into rest and safety. Darkness descended upon land and sea, washing away the harsh experiences of the day.

Ingrid stood speechless as they neared the majestic dock. Something like a soft, deep organ note came from a horn on the upper deck of the ship, repeating itself in short murmurs of reassurance as if it were a purring cat approaching the fireside. Coming into port is an exciting adventure!

10. The Conference

Safely docked, Papa picked up the large satchels and led the way up to the city's main thoroughfare.

"Follow me," he called to his own group. "*Ack,* it is good to get on dry land again, to feel the solid earth under your feet."

"*Ja,* say that," puffed Emma, walking directly behind him, the baby in her arms. Annie and Ingrid took their time; there was so much to see and their curiosity was far from exhausted. Reaching Superior Street, they set their luggage down and waited for a trolley.

What sights began to unfold as they stared through the windows of the swiftly-gliding vehicle, scenes they had never encountered even in their wildest imaginings. Large, colorful circus posters splashed across the huge boulders along the way. Elephants! Lions! Clowns! Papa knew the names. Two tremulous country girls forgot their shyness. They laughed, and shouted, and called to each other as they ran back and forth across the aisle, fearful of missing something. Tall buildings pointed skyward. On one side a towering hill held the homes of the city on its shelves and ledges. One feared that even a little shake of the hill would send them tumbling down into the large, gapping bay along the foot of the city. Papa and Emma, amazed at the utter self-forgetfulness of the girls, tried to quiet them, but this was no time for restraints.

"Here we must get off," called Papa, motioning to the conductor.

The trolley stopped at a street corner in the west end of town, and the little frontier band started up the sloping avenue. Somewhere on this hill were the homes they expected to visit.

"The Pilstroms will surely be surprised when they see me," said Emma, as they panted their way up the board walks to First Street.

"Pilstroms live on Fourth Street," Papa remembered. "There should be three more blocks to climb."

"*Ja, ack,* it will be good to get there," answered Emma, breathing heavily. "But where are you going to stay, Hanson?"

"Oh, I think we go to Charley Anderson up on Fifth." Papa, laboring with the satchels, paused to rest. The dark hill up ahead made him wonder if they would ever make it.

"The church homes will be crowded alright with so many outsiders in town for the conference, I'm afraid." Emma began to feel uneasy.

They came to a place where the board walks ended and a rough stairway led to the next street. When they reached Pilstroms' street, Papa suggested they rest a while. Looking over the city from the fourth terrace, the difficult climb offered its rewards. Here was enchantment not for tongue to tell. Here was the lighted city at their feet, with stretches of channels and bays broken by bridges and sandbars. Long piers reached out toward the Great Lake. Tomorrow they would see it in all its clear beauty by daylight. And beyond the bay, beyond the harbor lights, were the foghorns, the eternal, mystical foghorns, ever calling and answering from the misty deep.

"All those lights!" cried Ingrid. They had seen starlight and moonlight and a kerosene lantern in the night, but nothing like this. How had they all been lighted?

After depositing Emma and her belongings on Fourth Street, Papa and Ingrid continued their trudge for another block. Wearily they reached the fifth ledge and found Charley Anderson's house lit up from top to bottom.

"*Ja, men i all världen's tider,* who is coming here?" called Mrs. Anderson, as she met Papa and Ingrid at the door. "Come, Charley, quick! Here is Hanson from south shore!"

"*Kära hjärtans,* come in, come in," greeted Charley, rushing to meet them at the threshold.

Oh, it was nice to come in alright, but Papa could see here was a house full of guests, no doubt come in for the conference.

"We, too, have come to attend the conference," he explained. "But it isn't possible for you to take us in, that I can see."

"Talk never about that," said Mrs. Anderson, cheerfully. " 'Where there is room in the heart, there is room in the house.' We'll find a way; take off your coats and be at home."

Mrs. Anderson started for the kitchen. "We'll put the coffeepot on and fix something to eat. You must be starved by now."

Papa followed her into the kitchen. "I brought you something from the farm." Opening the Swedish satchel, he took out a large box. "Here is some of Mama's butter and a couple dozen eggs."

"*Ja, men* in all the world. You shouldn't have done that." Mrs. Anderson set the big package on the table and began opening it. "Oh, my, so much! *Ja,* this will be handy to have right now. Thousand thanks."

It was good to go to sleep that night, high up in the hills. Looking down from the window of the room where they slept, Ingrid thought the world had turned upside down with its starlit heaven at their feet. Duluth!

The next day was Sunday and the beginning of the big conference in the Mission Church on Second Street. There would be preachers, missionaries, organ music, and a large choir, things to see and things to hear. Mama had told Ingrid what greatness to expect. As a young woman from Sweden she had sung in the choir of this church. Little had she realized, then, how those beautiful anthems would someday serve as lullabies sung to the accompaniment of waves and winds far out along the shores of the Great Lake. Ingrid could still remember those evening lullabies. Now she was to see and hear a real choir with many voices blended into four-part harmony.

It was a glorious Sunday morning, and descending

the hill on the way to church was a new experience. On the sensitive air of the Sabbath morning came the first stroke of a bell from some high belfry, then another, and still another. In a few moments the whole earth seemed to throb and swell with the symphony of bells. It seemed as if heaven and earth were saluting each other.

Papa was in high spirits as he walked down the avenue alongside Charley Anderson and the other delegates. Although his black suit was faded and a bit threadworn, his face was glowing with happy anticipation. This was no time to bemoan his clothes.

As they entered the sanctuary of the church on Second Street, Papa took hold of Ingrid's hand, and the little girl in the plain blue cotton serge dress reaching down to her hightop shoes walked with Papa down the long aisle of the church. Papa wanted to sit near the front where he would miss nothing. Being somewhat hard of hearing, it was wise that he should. Hadn't he put forth great effort to get to the conference?

The aisle seemed endlessly long to Ingrid. So many people. She had heard her parents speak of Dry Goods Johnson, Meat Market Carlson, and Fish Dock Erickson, but who were all these others? Here were city people who lived in fine houses with dining rooms and parlors and sitting rooms and sidewalks; city people who could eat all the bananas and *apelsiner* they wanted; city people with ruffled skirts, and hats with pretty flowers and berries which shook daintily when they nodded in their fancy manners; city people who could talk and laugh easily, not one bit bashful. What the city wouldn't do for one!

Just then Papa gave Ingrid a gentle poke. "Don't stare so hard. People will think you are a greenhorn right from Sweden."

All at once a beautiful lady came walking down the aisle. Ingrid just had to turn around. She must be a very important person, for everyone looked at her. She carried some large sheets of music under her arm. As she stepped along gracefully, she nodded to people at her left and to people on her right and smiled so sweetly, not one bit bashful. She must be someone great. Ingrid would remember this incident always. "Someday I'm going to walk into our little country church like that," she said to herself. "I too shall nod to one side, then the other, and not be one bit bashful."

The lovely lady walked all the way up to the platform, and it became clear to Ingrid who she was.

"That's the organist," she whispered to Papa, her eyes filled with wonder. And sure enough, the young woman gracefully took her place before the large reed organ. Ingrid watched how she placed her feet, solemnly, on the foot pedals and how she pushed the swells apart with her knees. Her white hands drew out the proper stops, then dropped like winged birds to the ivory keys. Now the music began. It flowed into the sanctuary, first in a fine stream—tender, celestial—then grew in fullness until every nook and crevice in the house of worship throbbed with its rich volume. Ingrid watched every movement of the artistic performance, the organist's whole body assisting in the production. At times she would sit erect on the stool, then throw herself back slowly, like a wave gathering strength for the next leap upon shore. At such times she would pump wind into the organ with all the speed and strength her legs could muster. Other times she would fling herself over the keys in intimate communication. She played with her whole being.

In the music were starlight and waves, ripples spreading on shore and drawing back. Sometimes a phrase kept repeating itself, over and over, anxiously, like a trapped bird trying to find a way out. Ingrid would remember this, too, this part of the conference. How great was music! And what a moment for a timid country girl reaching out with all the tendrils of her soul.

A tall, dignified minister rose to his feet on the platform. Holding up the little gray hymnal, *Sionsharpan,* he announced that the meeting would begin with song number 174—"*Sabbatsdag, hur skön du är.*"

The congregation rose to sing—ministers, choir, old and young, Dry Goods Johnson, and Fish Dock Erickson. Here was a song of praise they all knew. It seemed to lift the very rafters of the church. All inner locks seemed broken, and hearts were free. Had the beautiful organ prelude inspired all this? One stanza flowed soulfully into the other.

Let Thy mighty Word hold sway
Over men on earth today;
Our poor souls, good Shepherd, feed,
Into pastures green us lead.

Ingrid looked up at Papa. He was singing, too, with all the voice he had. But his singing came from some place deep inside, for Ingrid saw a tear roll down his face, becoming lost in his long beard. Papa was already tasting of conference blessings. She remembered what Papa had said some days before when he talked to his neighbor, Isakson, about the coming conference. He had placed his hand on his breast as he spoke, "I feel a need in here. I must find something for the inner man."

The inner man. How often Papa had spoken those words. In this exalted hour of worship Ingrid felt she understood what he meant. Had not the power of song and music found a gateway into her own inner life? It touched her in the same indefinable way that once the cadence of a certain song had done. She recalled that mystical night back in the years of early childhood. Then, like now, all that was dark and harsh and vague was washed away and she was transported to some other world. "It must have been a foretaste of Heaven," Mama had said when she tried to explain it to her. That must be the way all these singing people feel right now, thought Ingrid. Perhaps everyone has a cadence somewhere, deep inside, that springs to life at a time like this.

Ingrid looked up into the faces of the people and, somehow, knew it was a great conference.

11. JUL PREPARATIONS

The first snowfall was swiftly followed by another, and still another, and soon the snow lay deep upon the land. Earth had taken on its usual change. After the violent tempests of November, the Great Lake lay silent under a thick floor of ice and snow. Having delivered its last stern lecture for the year, it had nothing more to say. And now it was December.

The men took off for the logging camps with their knapsacks, and the women and their youngest ones stayed close to their log houses, from whose chimneys pillars of smoke rose swifter and thicker each day. The days were often lonely and long, with a tiresome sameness.

Along the windswept Corduroy Road, Annie, Isak, and Ingrid could be seen each day beating their way to the little one-room country schoolhouse. From the gray of morning till the time of setting sun they would be gone from home, a good hour, or more, being required to walk the distance between home and school. Breakfast was eaten by lamplight, and it was almost time to light the lamp again when they returned at night. More than once in the sterner winter days, whether arriving at school in the morning or home at night, it was necessary to lay packs of snow on frostbitten cheeks, or feet, or hands. Fierce were the winter days for children tramping the long, snowy miles to school.

But for all that, in the little country schoolhouse they occasionally came face to face with greatness, true greatness—men like Longfellow, Whittier, Emerson, and others, to say nothing of George Washington and Abraham Lincoln. With eagerness and understanding they memorized and recited "The First Snowfall" by James Russell Lowell and "The Barefoot Boy" by Longfellow. *Ja, ack,* it was a time of strength, a time of flighting new wings of the spirit.

But back in the log homes on the shores, life was long and still, the children in school and the men off in the logging camps.

One morning in December Mama left her churn right in the middle of the kitchen floor and went to look out upon the day through the window facing Emma's house. *Ja,* it was good to have a window, to take one's eyes from small, cramped quarters and rest them on the vaster spaces. For over half an hour she had been stomping the dasher up and down in the churn, but the cream refused to turn to butter. Perhaps it was too thin, or something. But it felt good to rest her arms, and it was refreshing to look out upon the winter day—bushes and shrubs rolled into white softness, the spired firs silhouetted against a pale blue sky, their branches weighted with snow. And as she stood there, short thoughts gave way to long ones. Then what should she see? *Jojomen,* fluttering in and out among the frosted bushes was Emma and her gray, tasseled shawl. Yes, sir, coming along the trail was Emma! How did she ever get away from her two little ones? They must be napping, of course. "It's like sunshine coming through a rainy day to see the stirring of a human being coming toward your door this time of year," said Mama, even though little Anders was the only one to hear. She hurriedly tied on a clean apron and looked through the window again to see how near Emma was getting. But what in the world was she carrying? "*Ja,* you will see they have been butchering over there at Isaksons, and there is no end to Emma's generosity when she goes to giving something. How can one ever get even with such a one?"

"Good morning, Emma," saluted Mama, as she opened the door. "But what in the big world are you carrying so hard?"

Emma smiled as she walked heavily to the kitchen table and laid her burden down with a thud.

"But what, I say, have you brought?" persisted Mama, pretending not to have the slightest idea.

"Oh, it's nothing much. Just a little meat to fix for Christmas." Emma removed the white flour sack to expose a huge leg of veal.

"*Nej,* Emma. What are you thinking of? That is far too much. We settlers need to sell our meat for groceries. You shouldn't, Emma."

"Oh, it's only a little taste. We haven't had too much meat down here on the shores for some time now, and this is butchering time. We should enjoy meat while we have it." Emma removed her gray shawl and sat down. "You make yourself some *kalvdans* for Christmas," she added.

"*Ja,* thousand thanks, Emma. I will give you a little taste of pork when we butcher our pig." Mama slid the coffeepot forward on the stove. "*Ja,* thousand thanks again, Emma. It's too much."

"Talk never about that," said Emma, disregarding any mention of thanks or reciprocation. Just like Emma, thought Mama, as she went to the cupboard for cups and saucers. *Ja,* the Isaksons were pushing ahead. They need not worry if they don't sell the best meat on the hoof. Emma had always set a good table, even in the frugal days of the first years. But Emma had a generous hand, plump and kind, no denying that. It was easy for Emma to give. But *tacka för de,* they had more to take of.

December was butchering time on the shores. For Mama it was not a pleasant ordeal. "Imagine taking a creature you have learned to love, and who, in turn, has learned to trust you, and coldbloodedly transforming it into something tasty for man's stomach." With more prosperity in the stables, and Christmas coming on, the settlers' lean-to kitchens, or sheds, were sights to behold. Here were tubs, pails, crocks, and dishpans with bloody, ice-crusted waters in which all manner of animal organs lay in soak—hearts, kidneys, livers, stomach linings, tongues. Roasts, chops, and steaks were sold to the village store. What lay hidden under the choicer meats the settlers kept for their own tables, and thankful for that. These inner parts were cooked, chopped, mixed, and spiced into various kinds of *syltor,* head cheeses and sausages.

Intestines, yards long, lay sprawling in salt water. These were scraped, washed, turned inside out, and scraped again. Then they were blown up into long, snake-like balloons and stuffed with a mixture of ground meat and raw potatoes. A funnel cut from a cow's horn was inserted at one end of the casing to serve as a throat to channel the mixture into the long esophagus. When the casing was well filled, they called it *korv*. Swedish *korv*.

And that was not all. In one corner of the lean-to was a wooden bucket containing the animal's blood. This, too, must not be wasted. It was used in making a bread called *palt*. The dough, reddish in color, was rolled into round loaves with a large hole in the center, like a doughnut. When the loaves were baked and cooled, they were strung on a broom handle and hung above the stove to dry. Weeks later, on a gloomy day when the food supply was low, the hard loaves were dipped in hot water and served with a white, creamy gravy. The grown-ups fared well enough on this dish, but the children usually looked at it and drew back. "*Fy.*"

"*Vi får lära oss sätta mun efter matsäcken,*" Mama would say.

"Eat now, Ingrid," Papa would add. "Remember the starving children in China."

But neither suggestion did the trick, and the *palt* usually remained uneaten.

Ack, ja. And this was not all. On top of the rusty

stove stood a kettle of boiling water where pig hocks were scalded, then scraped, cooked, and pickled. And from the pig's head came the very choicest delicacy for the Christmas *kalas.*

"You poor animal," Mama would say, as its head lay in a tub of clear water, the eyes glaring, their last plea not yet gone out of them. From it came the finest *sylta* of all. After the head was split and cooked, rich pickings of meat were extracted from the bony crevices of the skull. These were made into a loaf tightly wrapped in cheesecloth and then placed in a mold with a flat iron set on top to press it firmly—*pressylta.*

"No, butchering time is a mess, a *röra,*" said Mama. "There is neither angel song nor silver tinsel till the last drop of blood is washed away."

The few odds and ends that were left of the animal, not at all edible for man, were cooked and mixed with cornmeal for the chickens to enjoy. Only something resembling a windpipe was actually tossed away. If the victim were a cow, the horns were sawed into pieces and were mighty handy to use as funnels when making *korv.* The hide of the animal made a lap covering good to have when riding in the cutter on a winter day. *Nej,* nothing must go to waste.

The weeks before Christmas were busy ones. One afternoon it behooved Mama to make some tracks in the snow for Emma's house. This time it was her turn to carry a good-sized parcel under her arm, although no match for the packs that Emma carried. *Nej, du,* but choice for all that. It was half a pig's head for *pressylta.* Nothing to be ashamed of.

It was a mild, sunny, winter day, a day that puts

summer right into your heart. A day that lights up memories and delicate sensations which you have felt at some turn in the road of the distant past.

"It's so much like Sweden, today," said Mama, as she entered Emma's happy kitchen with all its tantalizing fragrance. She set her errand on the table with finality, then with the corner of her white apron wiped away the bright snow tears from her eyes.

"*Ja,* you have said it. Haven't I felt Sweden all around me today?"

With Christmas approaching, thoughts of Sweden came back, warm and tender. Emma patted her large coffee dough down with a final punch and set it aside. Then the two women sat down and in memory walked the long way back to the old country, as they so often did this time of year. Warm wisps of yesteryears swept through the kitchen as they spoke of midnight suns and songs of nightingales. They lingered in their reminiscing to look once more upon the neat, red *stuga* which had once been home. Then all at once they stood beside the cool blue waters of Lake Vänern. *Ja,* they had both been there. And were you ever in the stores of Karlstad or Jönköping? *Jojomen.* And how beautiful was Sweden, nearing the time of *jul!* And so the afternoon swelled in wonder and enchantment, for drawing aside the draperies, separating past from present, has its own peculiar rewards.

"*Ja,* this has been a pleasant moment," said Mama, turning from the coffee table to go back to her own house.

There followed abundant exclamations and expressions of gratitude for the half of a pig's head on the kitchen table. It's too much, and you shouldn't have done it, and so forth.

"Now I must set my *enbärsdricka* the moment I get home," said Mama, starting for the door. "Juniper ale, they call it in America. It is so good to have if someone happens to travel down to the shores at Christmastime."

"*Ja visst,*" said Emma, going with Mama to the door. "And thousand, thousand thanks for what you brought."

"Talk never about that, and now good-bye with you, Emma, I must go." Mama drew a long, satisfying breath of winter air and started down the path.

Home again, she brought out her five-gallon crock. In a small jar were plump blackberries in soak, no longer dry and wrinkled as when purchased at the store in town. These, together with molasses, yeast, sugar, and warm water were poured into the large stone crock, where all was mixed and stirred and then covered and left in warm stillness for several days. *Enbärsdricka. Ack,* what a drink!

"*Jul* without *enbärsdricka* would be as bad as *jul* without a tree," said Ingrid, smacking her lips. She had chosen to sit up late to see how it was made.

"Now this ends the first chapter in our Christmas preparations," said Mama, as she hung the long-stemmed ladle on the wall above the stone crock and untied her apron for the day.

"*Ja,* think anyway, how much there is to do," she said, as she settled back on a chair to rest. "It wasn't like this in our earlier years."

But after all the raw smells and the cooked smells and the chopping, stuffing, grinding, and crock filling was over, the pantry shelves looked down on you in such a pleasant way. It was something accomplished—like having written a book. Mama had a pleased look coming through her weariness.

"Now let them come," she said—"settlers, town folks, Pastor Berg, and even President McKinley. There's a time of plenty in the Hanson log house on the shores. Now we go to bed, Ingrid."

12. THE FISHERMEN'S COTTAGE

Slowly the year turned from winter to spring, and the light winds of April began to fan across the wilderness. The land was young again and full of the breath of budding life and sun-thawed soil.

Dressed in an old, worn-out coat of her husband's and with a flour sack tied over her head, Mama set off for the Fishermen's Cottage up along the lake about three stone-casts to the east of her own abode. In one hand she carried a broom, in the other a large scrub pail rattling like a cowbell with its bar of Santa Claus soap and a scrub brush inside. Her swift movements suggested that something special was about to happen on the shores.

"Where in the big world are you going now?" asked Papa.

"I'm on my way to clean up the Fishermen's Cottage before the Axelbergs move in. They will be here next week, you know, and I want that they shall find a touch of homelikeness when they arrive. Goodness me, how those fishermen left the place last fall! It will take some real grit to get that dirt loose."

The Fishermen's Cottage and the land on which it stood belonged to the Hansons. Papa had built the cottage during the slack seasons of the year, using what material he had on hand and what he could find along the shores. During the autumn there were sometimes shipwrecks, and huge waves loaded with boards of all sizes, logs, boxes, barrels, and other debris were washed up on shore like dollars from heaven. *Ja,* this was not so little to get, tossed up, as it was, almost at your doorstep.

"Someone's loss, another's blessing," Papa would say. "It was not for nothing that I settled on these shores."

When the rough-boarded dwelling up along the lake had been finished, Papa had rented it for a paltry sum to some fishermen who came to these parts during the trout season. And so it got its name—the Fishermen's Cottage. Though it was not built for winter living, an occasional woodcutter might come along and ask for its use. With plenty of birchwood on hand, they managed to survive for the few days, or weeks, they were there. At times people from the Big City summered on the shores, and the cottage provided pleasant shelter close beside the splashing waves. In between longer periods of occupancy it was sometimes used for overnight guests when there were too many for the Hansons' own log cabin. Many a time Mama had scrubbed the wide pine-board floor of the front room and cozied it up for some traveling preacher who was glad to spend the night in solitude.

"Bring your satchels and follow me; I will show you where you will sleep tonight," Papa would say, as he led some itinerant Elisha by lantern light to the Fishermen's Cottage. It was not a little proud he was over the unusual luxury of an extra dwelling on the place. No more need the women argue and stew among themselves as to who should sleep the preacher. *Nej, du.* Papa wished he had built it earlier, for every preacher loved the privacy of this arrangement. Here beside the singing waters many a dream was born. On these gull-swept borders there was time to think and plan while nature's nocturnes accompanied sage thoughts.

And on nights like these another light dotted the forested shore. For here beside the glow of a one-wick lamp a servant of God might well be discovering new, lush paths within the Holy Scriptures. And as he waits on the Lord in prayer and meditation, what glory he encounters in the midnight stillness! A great truth springs forth—a message from the Word takes form!

Though the bare-boarded house along the shore looked somewhat apologetic and forlorn on the outside, it boasted of two rooms and a lean-to kitchen. But for overnight guests Mama concentrated on the front room only and closed the door to the other rooms. In this larger room, called the front room, was placed an iron bed, a washstand with a large crockery bowl and pitcher, and a table on which stood Mama's best kerosene lamp. On the floor lay a fluffy rag rug made with hundreds of odd pieces of cloth cut in tiny squares with one end tacked to a heavy backing which had once been a feed sack. Thick and soft and fluffy it was for bare feet to step on.

On the wall over the bed hung the Ten Commandments, set securely in a gilted frame. On the opposite wall was a temperance picture which tore one's heart with sadness. Mama was glad to remove it from her own walls, feeling no immediate need of its impact. Papa had purchased it from a traveling agent because it taught a lesson on the evils of drink.

"A temperance picture should be on the walls of every man's home," he said.

"*Ja*, that can well hang in the Fishermen's Cottage," said Mama, "for I found a queer looking bottle in the bushes outside the door." So Papa agreed to transferring the scene.

In one corner of the guest room was an old Franklin heating stove and close beside it a woodbox filled with wood, for the nights were cool by the lake even in the summer.

"How home-pleasant it looks," Mama would say, half aloud, after cleaning up the room and setting it in order for the next lodger. The well-patched curtains hung clean and starched. A bowl of wild flowers added brightness to the room. It was as though she were a little girl again playing house.

"I would give anything to sleep here myself," she said. "What peace, what solitude, the rolling waters soothing away all cares." It was even closer to the waters than her own house. Almost she wished she could trade. But the Fishermen's Cottage was not warm enough for family life in winter, it being built of rough lumber, not logs.

"*Ja,* think what a difference it makes when an empty, neglected shanty is made into a home. What a good feeling. It's like having painted a picture or written a poem. You just want to stand and look at it."

Jojo, Mama would have such a good time all by herself when she puttered in the other little house along the shore. One day, returning from the place, she resolved that she would take an afternoon off and bring Anders, Ingrid, and all her mending over to the cottage and spend the whole afternoon away from her own walls. She would also invite Emma. They would make coffee on the rusty kitchen stove in the lean-to, and it would be as much fun as visiting Sofie Monson four miles up in the hills. "You haven't more fun than you make for yourself," she mumbled as she started down the path toward home.

But that luxurious afternoon never seemed to come, for now the Axelbergs were moving into the cottage. She must get every corner of the house cleaned up before they moved in. Seven they were, and some pieces of furniture besides. The cottage would be full, alright.

How excited Mama was the morning she set off to clean the cottage. Passing her own root cellar, she hurried along a brief path which ended where a strip of slough flowed into the Great Lake. A second cousin of the Big Slough, I suppose, she thought to herself. No telling where his relatives might turn up in these parts. She walked cautiously along the log that bridged the stream and almost lost her footing when a sudden splash occurred in the marsh to one side of her. It could have been a muskrat or a woodchuck. It disappeared so fast into the tall grasses that she wasn't sure. But big he was, that she could tell. Near the end of the log some frogs lay basking in a pool of sunshine.

When safely across the strip of marshland, she entered the opening in the woods where the cows had begun a path. This was an inviting trail, curving left and right between trees of many kinds. Here and there the lake showed through. Its floats of ice had melted, and little waves sprang with rough joy on the sandy beach. In the distance two small boats had come to life again, having slipped out of their winter moorings.

Ja, it's fun, this walk to the Fishermen's Cottage, she thought—a path, a slough to cross, and then another path and you are there. All in a five-minute walk. There was something special in the mood of this April morning. Oh, it was going to be pleasant alright to have another neighbor to go and see. She hoped Mrs. Axelberg and she would get along well. What little she had seen of her, she thought she was nice. Warm and happy and pleasant to talk to. Born in Småland, Sweden, she had a special way of holding her r's. Kind of different from other Swedes.

You can believe there was cleaning to do the day she prepared for the new neighbors' arrival. Besides, there was furniture to remove from the front room, where preachers had sometimes slept. Papa would have to take care of that.

Ja, the Axelbergs. They had not had so rosy a path, thought Mama, as she lay on her knees scrubbing the floors. Poverty seemed never to have left their doorstep from what she had heard. But unlike most folk in their circumstances they seemed to ride victoriously on the crest of the waves and always appeared light and carefree. They had traveled a great deal since coming as newlyweds from Sweden. From Kansas they had gone to South Dakota and then to Minnesota and now to Wisconsin. They had been here but a short time when the house they occupied in town burned to the ground for reasons they could not help. So what should they do now? *Jojo.* That was when Papa appeared on the scene and offered them the Fishermen's Cottage. It being spring, the cottage would house them comfortably for six or seven months to come. By that time something else might be arranged.

"Just move in, it will cost you nothing," Papa informed them. "Here will be good ground for a garden plot, and all the wood you need you'll find along the shores, free for the gathering. Water you have in the great tank close to your door, and it never runs dry, the freshest, safest, coolest water in the world." Papa pointed toward the Great Lake, with a twinkle in his eye.

"*Ja,* can you think, Hanna," said Johan Axelberg, turning to his wife.

"This is of the Lord," answered Hanna, with a firm nod. "I knew something would turn up. It always does."

Papa marvelled at her faith. In spite of long years of adverse circumstances her flame of faith had never diminished.

Ja, someone is meant to be the Hannas in this world.

13. New neighbors

It was the middle of April when the Axelbergs moved down to the shores. New neighbors, new relationships, new feelings, a bit of new history.

The Axelbergs were a happy family. Mama and Emma couldn't quite make them out. Was it good to be so carefree in such circumstances as theirs?

"I don't see how they can take life so lightly," said Emma, coming over to borrow some sugar one afternoon.

"Well, they are Smålänningar, they are birds of a different feather," supposed Mama.

"*Ja,* but after all they have gone through, you would think they would feel like giving up. But not the Axelbergs."

"Did you hear the horn music this morning?" asked Mama, her face both puzzled and amused. "It doesn't sound as if they were sitting under any cloud. Early, before we were up, Axelberg was on top of the lean-to kitchen roof tooting his horn to beat the ban'."

"*Ja visst,* heard I that; who could sleep? So that was Axelberg. I thought it came from the direction of the Fishermen's Cottage. Where do you s'pose he got hold of that?"

"Oh, that he has carried with him for years, Mrs. Axelberg told me. Whatever else they've lost he has clung to that horn with all his might. And he isn't so bad to play. He gave quite a tooting melody this morning. You should have seen the crows and the meadowlarks. They were swooping wildly in dark numbers all around us. I think they were wondering what kind of a bird had landed in this wilderness. *Nej,* we couldn't sleep. Papa got up and dressed. Then he walked down the shore toward the Fishermen's Cottage, and what did he see? Yes, siree, right on top of the kitchen roof sat Johan Axelberg tooting like everything, as if he had the whole world for his audience. Papa didn't go near the house, and they didn't know he was spying through the bushes. But when Papa was making a fire in the kitchen stove, I heard him chuckling to himself out there. You know, Papa isn't much for laughter."

"I hope they don't carry this tooting too far. I don't like to have the little ones wake up so early. It must have been five o'clock when he began this morning." Emma nipped a dead leaf off Mama's geranium and got up to go.

"*Ja,* it was five minutes to five when he began, but it isn't so unpleasant to wake up to something besides wind and waves—*blåst å böljor.* Anyhow, I heard Mrs. Axelberg say that he always greeted the first day of the week with horn music. Kind of nice, Emma. It will not be every day." Mama jerked the coffeepot forward as if it had fallen asleep on the job.

"Don't go yet, Emma," she said, pulling out the old cane rocking chair. "There is more yet to talk about."

"Oh, Emma, they are so happy over there in the Fishermen's Cottage. I never saw anything like it." Mama's face softened with a touch of sadness as she spoke. "Mrs. Axelberg is a real Christian alright, that I can see. She has some faults, no doubt, but joy she has in unusual measure. In all their uncertainties she seems so confident, and her life is packed with daily surprises that none of us seem to see. I wish you could hear her sing! She knows no end of beautiful hymns by heart. I can hear her when she goes down to the lake for water, or when she gathers driftwood on the shore. It is a voice with beauty and longing, something unusual. Help yourself to cream and sugar, Emma."

"*Ja,* think anyway, another neighbor. Who would have thought that day would ever come!" Emma looked out of Mama's window into far horizons. "No doubt this will bring some changes down here on the shores for both old and young. It is as if a new door had opened." Then it was time for Emma to go home.

* * * *

"*Jojo,* here I could live forever," said Mrs. Axelberg on the first Sunday in their home on the shores. The Hansons had been invited over there for the afternoon.

It was a delightful day with the lofty feel a Sunday afternoon brings when there is a special plan in the air. A new neighbor to visit and only a short path between! That was something. A soft April mist hung in the air, and the breath of greening life added zest to the occasion as the Hansons started down the path to the home of their new friends. There was a feeling of rest and relaxation, a sense of expectancy. Even the sun had its Sunday afternoon smile on, the kind just made for April. Life was expanding.

From her small kitchen window Hanna saw her guests emerge from the wooded path. She hurried out to greet them.

"Good afternoon and welcome to our home," she called, and there was warmth in both her voice and countenance as she gave each one a hearty handshake. It was much like Sofie Monson's greetings, thought Mama.

Ingrid soon shed her timidity as she was taken in hand by Gudrin, Olga, Hans, and Oscar. Oh, she must come and see the bridge they had made! And the log cabin in the woods! And the little graveyard where two dead birds were buried! And, oh, there was the best place to play "homestead" in the woodland west of the house where a new crop of spruces and balsams stood young and green, replacing the ancient ones which had seen their day and gone the way of all life! It would be exciting to play homestead!

The clumps of small trees made delightful hiding places, and everyone chose his own sequestered spot. It was fun finding each other and making paths between each haunt. To make their habitations cozy and attractive they gathered stones from the lake shore – quartz, felspar, granite, and even little agates. To find an agate was good luck. From the forest came mosses and bark and cones of all sizes. Boxes and barrels from off the beach became furniture. The woodland became alive with childhood ideas. They who had never known the luxury of owning heaps of shining toys and baubles, of having readymade playtime gadgets and equipment, to them the playtime hour became a time of great creation, and in creating their imaginations grew. And what they could not think of as they pooled ideas and suggestions! Nature was their playground, their source of inspiration, and their teacher. Ingrid felt a new significance to every common thing around.

Inside the Fishermen's Cottage there was no lack of high spirit, either, as Johan Axelberg took over the conversation and began relating some of the humorous adventures he had encountered in life. Johan enjoyed talking. He was a master at decorating his tales with high color. Papa and Mama listened eagerly and tried to laugh a little with him, for, after all, here was a new voice, a new face, and vivid descriptions from new, far-off places. Something different. Occasionally Hanna would interrupt her husband with a brief word of caution—"Now, Johan, you are going too far."

The scantily furnished rooms were cozy and clean here at the Axelbergs, thought Mama as she looked around the place. Hanna had curtained off one end of the middle room, converting it into a sleeping room. Not so dumb. Early marsh marigolds shone like lamps of sunshine all about the place. Even the lean-to kitchen was pleasant and sunny with a brisk fire in the old kitchen stove. Somehow the fire in

Hanna's stove had a special glow. It was pleasant here, alright.

"So you think, Mrs. Axelberg, you would like to live here on the shores always?" asked Papa, when Johan paused for a second to light his pipe.

"*Ja*, here I could live and die. I have already made friends with the Great Lake, though I don't understand all his moods. But to go to sleep with the song of the waves, that is something I've never known before. And how good one sleeps!" Mrs. Axelberg rose to go into the kitchen, and before long everyone knew what she was doing.

"Can I help you out there?" called Mama. But Hanna Axelberg wanted Mama to be company this afternoon and just rest.

"You look at that plush album on the bureau, Mrs. Hanson. In it you will find photographs of all our relatives in Småland."

In no time the table was set for six children and four grown-ups, and there was an instant sense of high festivity in the air as they all gathered around the coffee table. Johan Axelberg added touches of mirth to the conversation, and there was pleasantness at the Axelberg table.

The sun was beginning to fling a golden bridge across the lake, and the stillness of evening came on. Hanna Axelberg brought out the well-worn Bible and handed it to Papa.

"Now let us see what God has for us before the day is over," she said, seating herself at the table again. Hanna believed firmly that the fear of the Lord is the beginning of wisdom. She taught this to her children, and she quoted it to her husband, who was less sensitive to the ways of the spirit. This divine wisdom had given direction to her own inner life in spite of the contrary aspect external circumstances often presented. Her trial of faith had been rewarded by a growth of strength and courage which characterized her Christian life.

Papa opened the Bible to the ninety-first psalm; he read it meaningfully, then closed with prayer.

"Before we part, won't you sing for us a song, Mrs. Axelberg?" begged Mama. "I know you have many songs warm off the heart."

"Yes, there isn't a day that I don't pull out the rocker and sit down and sing. Looking out upon the Great Lake it comes easy to sing."

"*Ja*, they that can do that," said Mama. "The first years after we moved on our homesteads I used to take time off to sing, too. But as the fields and herds grew larger, the days seem to grow shorter. If I sing at all, it must be while I work."

"But you must take time to learn new songs, Mrs. Hanson," admonished Hanna. "Let the work stand. That is my way of visiting with the Lord, and I come away refreshed and strong for the day's demands. No, sing I will, whatever else happens." Hanna rose from the table and sat down in the familiar rocking chair and began to sing.

It was an English song that she chose, unknown to Papa and Mama Hanson but beautiful for all that. Hanna had memorized it, and though some words were not familiar to either singer or listener, they somehow knew what was meant. Her voice rose clear and soulful as she surrendered herself to the song. Hers was a voice rich with emotion and with an indomitable note of triumph. It came through her voice, through the words, and through the rapt expression on her face.

So this is the secret of Hanna's happy life, thought Mama, as she listened. She sweeps away her trials with the burst of song.

My Father is rich in houses and lands,
He holdeth the wealth of the world in his hands . . .

Hanna's voice rang with the conviction that she was a child of a King.

A tent or a cottage, why should I care?
They're building a palace for me over there . . .

The gold in the western sky faded into a soft afterglow, and darkness began to descend on the Fishermen's Cottage. But as Hanna sang, the humble dwelling on the shore seemed to be flooded with a thousand lights while heaven and all the world outside drew near and listened.

Though exiled from home, yet still I may sing:
All glory to God, I'm the child of a King.

The child of a King. . . . The child of a King. . . . The words rang through the woods as the Hansons walked the path to their home that night. It was good to have some Hannas in this world.

In the turn of the trail Ingrid looked back, and through an aisle in the trees she saw a light. Hanna had set a lamp in the window. Another beam on the wild, dark shore. Again she felt that tug of the heart, the flutter of a wing trying to find an open door. A lamp against the dark . . . the child of a King. . . .

14. Cranberry

A name fitly chosen is an accomplishment. Cranberry. That was the name given to the settlement up along the shores about seven miles to the east of the Hanson homestead. Just a little fringe of a colony it was, a lapful of immigrants who had trickled in from the shores of Finland. The immensity of green forests and azure waters held a magic appeal for them, being so much a part of the wild silence of Old Finland.

"*Ja,* birds of a feather flock together," said Mama. They were a different brand of people. No denying that. With a passion for open spaces, they built their huts as close to the far-flung sea as they dared. Here in little knots they huddled together in pleasant intimacy with the Father of Waters. They were a colorful people, but untamed in temperament, and brawls were not uncommon. Their capacity for enduring hardship was touching to see. Living on the margins of nothing, they had trained themselves to exist stoically on the slimmest necessities.

"But talk they can when they get together," observed Mama. "Loud and fast, their r's rolling like grease. But 'One must cackle with the beak one has.' Likely it's as the sheep shearer says, 'Much noise and little wool.' "

Evening had come, and Mama was drying her supper dishes in the semi-darkness to save on kerosene. Papa remained seated at the supper table. He was in a talkative mood, for something good had come his way.

"*Jo,* the man that christened that little colony knew what he was doing. You can be sure he had tramped that country up and down." Papa got up to light his lantern, for there was the barn work yet to do.

The land up along the shore to the east of the Hansons was pitted with swamps and sedges which turned up in the most unexpected places, winding in and out in irregular manner yet following close to the side of the lake. And where there is a swamp there may well be a yield of the tart red fruit called cranberries. You don't find the first berries easily, but when you do, you discover they come in neighborly fashion. Where there is one, there is another, and another, as your eye gets trained to see them.

"*Jojo,* there is a strong likeness between the cranberry patch and the Finnish way of settling," said Papa, closing the door behind him.

The little hamlet up along the scalloped shore had drawn together warmly—first one, then another, and another. *Ja,* Cranberry was a fitting name alright.

But how they came to talk about Cranberry that evening was that a stroke of good fortune had come their way. Papa had qualified for the job as mail carrier between his own town and the little Finnish settlement. Any job was enviably precious if it produced a check at the end of the month. Clearing land and breaking soil brought no cash to lay one's hands on. The butter and eggs barely paid for groceries. So when Papa got the mail route to Cranberry at twenty-four dollars a month, the sun came out all over the Hanson place. How good would be the feel of a few dollars in a purse that usually had nothing in it but the smell of old leather!

Jojo, three times a week—Tuesday, Thursday, and Saturday—for a term of four years, Papa was to hitch up his horse and set off for Cranberry with a canvas bag of mail. Oh, there would be packages, and crates, and sacks of feed to haul too, and there would be other extras for which he would receive little or nothing for the trouble of handling. If people were poorer than the poor, he would say, "Oh, that's alright, I had to make the trip anyhow." But always there would be the twenty-four dollars at the end of the month.

"*Ja,* there is nothing like working for Uncle Sam," declared Mama with the nod of one who knew. Now long-desired things were going to happen. "There's a big change come on since that Cleveland got out and President McKinley is at the head," she said.

When Mama told Ingrid about the good turn of events, there was only one question in Ingrid's mind. "Will we get our organ now?"

"*Ack,* it will take more than one check to get an

organ, but if we all help and save a little here and a little there, it's just possible that we can make it. We will see what Papa says."

So Tuesdays, Thursdays, and Saturdays Papa was up early. First he had to go to town to get the Cranberry mail sack and load up with other dray. Then he had to come halfway home to where a road climbed southward into the hill country, passing not too far from Sofie Monson's hut. It was the long way round, of course, but all the newly-opened roads meandered in strange fashion, as if they didn't know their own minds. Seven miles to Cranberry? *Ja,* talk never about that. That was if you figured the distance in a straight line. The road to Cranberry was almost twice that long.

"The worst thing about the road to Cranberry is that awful Talbot's Hill," said Papa one evening, tired from his hard trip. He had hauled the mail in storms and fair weather, for several weeks now.

Ack, Talbot's Hill! In spring and fall, when the mud was high, it was his enemy number one.

"There's no time to enjoy the beauty of nature when you climb Talbot's Hill," he said; "it's just to keep your thoughts on the heights ahead." And then he added sadly, "What hard hills there are to climb in life before the road is finished."

"That's like the Corduroy Road, isn't it," said Ingrid, pensively, as she looked up from her book. She was reading *Under the Lilacs,* by Louisa Alcott, but anything related to Cranberry made her pause and listen. She couldn't forget that twenty-four dollar check and the possibilities it held of fulfilling her fondest dream.

"*Ja,* it's the steepest and longest hill in the country," Papa continued. "But, oh, what beauty when once you get to the top!"

Up on the summit of Talbot's Hill lived the bachelor for whom the hill was named. His little shack looked out upon the heights in peace and loneliness. But when a traveler chanced to reach the top of the hill, out he would come from his tar-paper dwelling as excited as a spider coming out of his curled leaf to investigate what manner of fly or gnat he has caught in his web. Many were the talks they had together, Papa and Talbot, on top of the hill while Papa was getting his breath. For going up Talbot's Hill required getting out of the wagon and walking beside old Walter, the horse. If the wagon was heavily loaded, it meant walking behind it, so that whenever Walter paused to rest, Papa could place a stone under each of the hind wheels to lessen the strain on his faithful companion.

"*Nej,* going up Talbot's Hill is no picnic, but there is God's glory to see from the top, wonders we cannot see down here on the flats. And to get a long drink from Talbot's cool spring—that, too, is something." Papa wound the clock and prepared for bed. "Yes, sir, a road in the wilderness has many chapters." Papa paused in the doorway as though he had more to say. Mama was busy setting bread and Ingrid, having laid her book aside, sat thinking about the road to Cranberry and all the hard, yet fascinating, experiences Papa encountered.

A hill has two slopes, and after riding along the high plateau on Talbot's place, it meant coming down to earth again on the other side. That was not so difficult, Papa explained, for on the other side there was fine gravel and less mud. At the foot was a secluded valley in which one little log hut stood desolate and lonely. Here was where the Carmichaels lived—Mr. and Mrs. They were not Swedes, but Papa didn't mind the Irish in them. Often he was asked into their cabin for a cup of tea. They seemed, somehow, to belong to this quiet valley as much as the little man on the hill belonged to the windswept heights. Hungry to see people, they kept their eyes fixed on the hill every Tuesday, Thursday, and Saturday, eagerly waiting for a black horse and a loaded wagon to come rumbling down the stony slope. Papa's brief stops were the bright moments in their week. Usually he had some settlement news to share, and even a morsel of world news from *Veckobladet.*

The Carmichaels were Catholics, but that didn't matter to Papa. He felt there was a special outreach of soul that made them one with him. *Ja,* stopping at the Carmichaels was refreshing for both sides. And if it was summer, the luscious rhubarb pie served with the tea was nothing to turn down when a man was beginning to feel hunger pains. Often Papa would leave a Bible quotation as he continued his journey. This was accepted with a tender smile and an understanding nod. And as they stood in the doorway watching the mail driver disappear over the hill, they thought of the desolate miles he must travel every Tuesday, Thursday, and Saturday. Loneliness has a way of knowing its own.

Nej, ack, the way to Cranberry was not paved with gold. There were streams to cross, over which crude, uncertain bridges had been flung, and in the spring of the year there were frost boils and wash-outs and places where the red clay was as slippery as pork grease. Sometimes a giant tree lay beaten across the road, requiring both ax and saw to remove, not to mention strength of muscle and depths of patience. *Nej,* the road to Cranberry was not paved with gold. It took something to be a mail driver.

But Papa received a check each month—twenty-four dollars—and that was nothing to sniff at. It was to feed all manner of hopes and dreams.

One evening Mama had a talk with Papa. It was an occasion she had long waited for, always feeling for the right time. It was not on the night of a Cranberry day. *Nej, du.* It was on a Sunday evening when he was rested and more approachable.

"Now, Hanson," she began, never calling him by his first name, Daniel. "This check you are getting each month, do you think we could set aside a few dollars, now and then, towards the organ Ingrid has wanted for so long?"

"Organ!" roared Papa. "It is all I can do to pay for the plow and harrow that I bought last year. And I need to save for a cultivator, and we should be thinking of a cream separator. There are so many, many things. *Ack, ja.* And you who are so *praktisk,* asking for an organ of all things."

"But think, anyway," urged Mama, "if Ingrid learns to play, she can be organist for our meetings in the church. That would be no small help. We wouldn't need to ask a Lutheran to play for us every time we have a service."

"And have you thought of how and where she's going to learn to play?"

"Oh, she can learn to chord by herself. You can get an organ book that shows you how. Besides, I hear the millwright who is coming to town has a daughter that is a real piano player. They say she will even have a piano with her when she comes. Wouldn't it be wonderful if Ingrid could take a few lessons from her? Think! To have a daughter that can play!"

"*Ja,* we will see." Papa had begun to yield. "I am as anxious as you that Ingrid shall have advantages we never had." Mama felt she had covered a long distance in one evening.

So Papa kept going—Tuesday, Thursday, and Saturday—a black horse, a loaded sleigh or wagon, and a driver with a long red beard. Southward along the countryside they moved, over hills and through deep valleys, then turning eastward over plains and marshes. Twenty-four dollars!

And always with the job was the inevitable testing of one's strength and patience—mud and ice, storms and lonely silences, washouts and windfalls, winter and snowdrifts—*ja,* snowdrifts!

And back home in the log cabin a girl dreamed. The miracle of an organ shone on the far-off horizon. She could see it. She could hear its rich tones, she could feel the touch of the snow-white keys—and she would almost weep with delight.

Coming home from Cranberry on a cold winter evening when night stood close, Papa wondered if he could hold out till the four-year term was up. It had been a hard day. Snow had fallen upon snow until the road was heaped with drifts. Time and again he had come up against a mountain of white only to have to crawl out of the sled and hew it down with his shovel so that the horse and sled could come through. This had taken hours out of the day. Too exhausted for words, he came home with no utterance but a long sigh. His back ached and burned, and the memory of the day weighed heavily on his heart.

Not until he had eaten and surrendered himself to the warmth and comfort of home did he feel able to relate some of the bitterness of the day.

Ingrid's heart bled for Papa. For a few moments she was able to set aside some of her own high hopes. She knew, in her own small way, some of the harshness Papa had suffered. She too had trudged the Corduroy Road in the drifts of mid-winter.

15. Ten dozen thimbles

It was almost midnight. A lamp still shone in the Hanson window up along the shores. *Jojo*, something was going on over there, an important matter to ponder. And in the dark hush of the autumn night Mama was trying to show Ingrid how to open a door to the solution.

"It's a good chance for you, Ingrid. In this way you can help Papa save money, for the less we need to draw on the twenty-four-dollar check the more we can lay aside for the organ," Mama reasoned.

That was true, and Ingrid was sorely in need of a winter coat. The old plush hand-me-down from Aunt Augusta had lost both color and shape. She had never liked it. She could not use it another winter. From the first day she had worn it she had longed for the day when she could have a coat like some of the other girls in school were wearing.

Mama pushed up close to Ingrid and pulled the kerosene lamp toward them. "You see this advertising? It says if you sell ten dozen thimbles at ten cents apiece you can clear a neat sum for yourself." She pointed to the little insert in the farm magazine. "Four dollars. That should give you enough money to pay for the winter coat in Sears and Roebuck's catalog." She picked up the catalog, which opened at once to the page they had feasted their eyes on for almost a year.

"But I don't want to sell thimbles," said Ingrid. "I don't know what to say. Where shall I go? I don't like to talk to people about thimbles."

"No, you don't like to talk to people at all. You are too shy. You know, there are times when you must set your face like a flint as you go through life. Remember the Corduroy Road. To do what's hard builds character." Mama picked up the magazine again and looked at the ad.

"Now when the thimbles come, you can begin selling them from house to house in town, after school, or during the noon hour when you have eaten your lunch," advised Mama. "Go first to the homes of people you know, then when you get on to it, you will have courage enough to go to the homes you don't know. You'll be surprised how it will work."

Ingrid and Mama spent several hours the next day writing a voluminous letter to the farm journal and concluded by ordering the ten dozen thimbles. When the letter was sealed and stamped, they set to work studying the catalog again. A new coat! What an event! There on the worn page it stood in all its glory. You could order it in one of three colors —red, black, or mouse gray. Ingrid wanted a red coat. But Mama said red would fade too soon and black was too old. "We will have to choose mouse gray. That will not show fade so much. Gray is a practical color. *Ja visst.*"

Over and over they read the fascinating bit of literature which accompanied the picture in the catalog—"Soft, warm, melton cloth, pleasant to the touch. . . . Any girl would be proud to wear it. . . . Comfortable for the coldest winter days. . . . Lined in old rose sateen. . . . No. 077D 5301. . . . Price, $3.98. . . . Colors: red, black, or mouse gray. . . . Be sure to state size and color."

In the catalog the coat was worn by a charming school girl who held her head high and posed her arm in a graceful gesture. *Jojo,* that was something to copy, thought Ingrid. She would stand like that when she wore her coat. That would make the school kids take notice. But mouse gray! "If it were only red," she pleaded.

"You don't have to tell anyone it's mouse gray," consoled Mama. "Call it winter gray, or silver gray, or kitten gray. Any gray name except mouse."

"But they all have Sears and Roebuck catalogs in their homes. If the kids look up the coat and find out we chose mouse gray, they will call me 'Mouse Skin.' They call Nels Larson 'Lard Can' because he is so fat, and John Swanson 'Bean Pole' because he is so skinny. Andy Johnson they call 'Andy Over.' And ever since the Axelbergs got a team of oxen they call Hans 'Oxtail.' But 'Mouse Skin!' I hope they don't find out. My coat is silver gray."

"That's right, stick to silver gray. I can't imagine what Sears and Roebuck thought of when they stuck a word like mouse gray in their advertising." Mama laid the catalog away, a little provoked.

"It's because everybody knows what shade that is. Everyone knows the shade of gray a mouse has. Haven't they all had mice in the house and in the barn and in the field?" Ingrid rose from the table with determination. "My coat is silver gray, and that's that."

Two weeks later the box of thimbles arrived, packed neatly in layers of twelve, and Ingrid knew she was to start her career as a thimble agent. It was to get experience, Mama had said, but Ingrid didn't give a hoot for experience. Her only incentive for tackling this forbidding task was to aid the fulfillment of her dream. She would fix her eyes always on the goal—the organ.

"You must be polite now, Ingrid," informed Mama on the first day Ingrid set out to sell thimbles. "Make people like you, and they will buy, you'll see. Don't forget your 'thank yous' and always say 'yes, ma'am,' and 'if you please.'" Papa helped Ingrid with her thimble speech, but Ingrid wasn't much impressed with the lingo she was to repeat ten dozen times, or maybe a hundred dozen times, before her sales experience was finished. "Good morning, Mrs. Nelson," she was to begin, unless it was afternoon or evening. "I have some extra fine thimbles to sell. There are big ones and small ones, and they fit nicely on any kind of finger. You can buy one, or many," This said, she was to hold the box up to the prospective buyer.

Her first day of selling along the main street of town wasn't as awful as she had expected. She sold two thimbles to Swanson's Grocery, and they even said to come back later and they might buy one more.

Then she sold three to Salberg, the shoemaker; to Bensons one; to Greenwoods another. And even old man Florie, who lived right up against the Big Slough, bought one.

"You see she has some business talent, alright," said Mama as she and Papa were mending a harness beside the kitchen stove that evening. They thought Ingrid was asleep, but she heard what they were saying in the kitchen.

"She will outgrow her bashfulness. She has always been so folk-scared, like hiding behind a bush on the way to school whenever she saw someone coming. No, selling thimbles will help her." Papa continued his work in silence, and Ingrid didn't know what he was thinking.

But the next day! Would she ever forget the next day! She had finished her lunch and placed the lid back on her two-quart syrup pail. There was still a half-hour left before the first bell would ring. She could go down one of the side lanes in town and perhaps sell a few thimbles before the last bell. She would take the lane to the left this time. There lived Mrs. Brask, first house down. Mrs. Brask did laundry work for the men at the logging camp. Ingrid knew that no one liked Mrs. Brask. Mama said life had been hard on her and that its hurts had made her bitter. Her face showed no marks of pleasure, and people stayed away from her, which only made the lines of bitterness deeper. But Ingrid wasn't going to pass up one house in town. She had ten dozen thimbles to sell, and there weren't enough houses to go around as it was, unless some people bought several. *Nej*, not by a long ways. It was different when

Annie sold stickpins. That was only a box of fifteen, and they were pretty to behold with all kinds of shiny jewels—rubies, sapphires, emeralds, and even diamonds. People's eyes were more tempted by a pretty stickpin. It would trim up their clothes, and that was sometimes worth a hard-earned dime. *Ja*, stickpins sold good. But ten dozen thimbles, that was something else. No, she couldn't pass up a single house. She would try Mrs. Brask's place and get it over with. "Set your face like a flint," Mama had said.

She turned the corner on Main Street and set off for Mrs. Brask's house. It was a cold day, and a large, white belly of a cloud hung in the sky. That meant more snow. She hoped the first bell wouldn't ring too soon, for then she would have to run like everything to get to school before the last bell sounded.

Barely had she reached Mrs. Brask's gate when a door swung open with a fierce screech and Mrs. Brask's face shot out like the Jumping Jack Anders got for Christmas, only the face was more scary. It seemed like a frightful windstorm had suddenly come loose. Clouds of wash-tub steam pushed through the open door, but for all that Mrs. Brask's face stood out clear and full above the mist. And her voice was unmistakably clear, full, and frightening.

"If you are selling something, you needn't come a step closer," she yelled, and slam, bang, screech went the door. Somewhere, nearby, a dog let out a terrifying bark.

Ingrid stood petrified. Time stopped. Would she ever wake up from this horrible moment! She couldn't think where she was until she heard the clang of the first bell. Then she came back to her senses. From somewhere came a voice: "Set your face like a flint." She walked back to school not caring if she ever got there, last bell or not. Where had the noon period gone, and not a thimble sold? She had lost all heart for everything.

In the arithmetic class that afternoon the teacher gave an oral test:

"If you had ten dozen pencils and sold them at ten cents apiece, how much would you get? Anybody?" Silence. Annie poked Ingrid with her finger and whispered from behind, "If anyone should know the answer, you should."

But Ingrid couldn't for one moment forget a certain face, a certain voice, and a cloud of vapor billowing through a certain door.

"You can tell it isn't in her," said Papa in the still of that night after Ingrid had gone to bed. "She has no talent for business. Too sensitive."

"Much like her father," answered Mama, doubling the speed of her knitting needles. "The apple doesn't fall far from the tree!"

But Ingrid was not sleeping. She heard every word. Who was she really like—Mama or Papa? Mama wasn't so little shy herself. Whenever a minister came to their home, her face would turn red all over. But she was practical and wanted to get ahead. So did Papa, yet people said he was not practical like Mama. He was the worst pusher in town when it came to some worthy cause—better roads, a new school, aid to some settlers in dire circumstances, money for the mission field in Alaska. And he didn't mind going ragged while he was pushing the issues.

"I wonder if anyone will ever thank you for all your

work and sacrifice and sleepless nights," said Mama one evening when Papa came home exhausted from the contentions at the town meeting.

"What the days can't understand, the years will make clear." That was all he said. Ingrid remembered the words.

One evening at the supper table Papa asked Ingrid if she wouldn't like to go with him to Cranberry on Saturday and see what luck she'd have selling thimbles to the Finns.

"We will go to the logging camp over there too. Men who are working there have money in their pocketbooks. You might sell not so few in the camp."

Ingrid had long wanted to go to this quiet little town up along the lake. She was curious to see the people Papa had so often spoken of. They had such funny names—Korpa, Milka, Reipi—and others. *Ja,* she would go with Papa to Cranberry.

It was winter and cold that January morning when Ingrid and Papa set out for Cranberry—mail bag, feed sacks, bob sleigh, and all. Ingrid sat with Papa in the front seat, her box of thimbles held securely on her lap under the thick horse blanket. Dawn had blossomed into a radiant sunrise by the time they ascended the hill country. Once beyond Talbot's Hill and the Carmichael valley there were long, open stretches of white loneliness.

After many miles of silent riding, they came in view of a small patch of habitation. Seen from the last bleak hill, the warmth of civilization was good to the eye. There in the plain below, its snow-quilted roofs huddled together in winter snugness, was the little settlement called Cranberry.

Papa pulled slightly at the reins, and old Walter stopped instantly and remained a dark statue against the sullen sky. He must have stopped here often, thought Ingrid, for he seemed to sense it was the thing to do. "We'll sit here a while," said Papa.

The earth was sealed in sinless white. Everything was wrapped in winter. Dry clumps of wayside fireweeds were richly dipped in white frost. Soft pillows of snow lay snugly on stumps and fence posts. The shore of the Great Lake below them was a magic city of alabaster towers and palaces. Here was beauty and sadness, life and death, paradoxically mingled in the winter wonderland below them. As they sat huddled together on top of Cranberry hill, that January day, Ingrid could feel that in that poignant moment Papa and she were one.

"It is a scene like this," said Papa, pointing with his mittened hand, "that makes one feel that some kind, unseen hand is loosening all the chains of our being—body, mind, and soul." Ingrid felt she understood. She felt this way when she heard music too—an untying of inner bands.

Any stir in the scene below brought a quickened warmth to their hearts—spirals of smoke from low roof tops . . . a rabbit's leap in the snow . . . a wolf scampering across the frozen lake . . . a woodsman with an ax on his shoulder, forest bound. . . . For each stir the scene deepened in beauty.

"Lord, make me to know mine end and the measure of my days, what it is," quoted Papa, prayerfully. Ingrid knew it was a bit of wisdom drawn from the Book of Books. With a slight pull of the reins, the horse started slowly down the long hill.

When they arrived at the narrow-shouldered building which served as store and post office, Papa took out his mail bag and started for the door.

"Now you must remember to be polite to the post office lady. Mrs. Loomas will no doubt buy some thimbles for her store."

Ingrid set her face for act one and came in with a big, made-to-order smile. Papa threw a glance at his daughter and knew the cost of timidity. Ingrid made her speech, showed her thimbles, and, much to her surprise, got an order for one whole dozen. Such a nice lady! Ingrid's smile became more natural now. She shook hands with the post office lady three times before she left, and Papa thought she must have spoken a dozen thank-yous by the time they closed the door behind them.

"My, Cranberry is a good place to sell thimbles in," Ingrid sighed happily as she and Papa walked back to the sled.

"Now we will drive to the logging camp for our dinner," said Papa. "There you will be able to sell thimbles to the lumberjacks. They will have cash in their pockets. A new thimble for the wife for Christmas might be something they hadn't thought about."

About a half mile inland from the lake stood a low, sprawling log building set deep in the woods and half buried in snow. Here in a large eating room long-haired and coarse-bearded loggers sat at their noontime meal, their tin plates piled high with camp food. Tin cups and tin knives and forks graced the bare boards of the table. Large bowls of beans and salt pork were passed and greedily accepted. For a moment Ingrid wondered if she had been transported to another planet. Here among the pineries were men from far parts of the country, their faces—what could be seen above their beards—red and leathery from much exposure to the stern elements.

The room was full of strange odors. Camp smells are unforgettable smells. The resinous odors of pine-wood freshly cut clung to the place. It was fastened to the men's plaid shirts; it was in their hair and whiskers; it even clung to their skin. Mixed with it were the odors of salt pork, baked beans, and Arbuckles coffee, long in the brewing. There were fresh whiffs and stale whiffs of pipe smoke and La Turka tobacco, and under the large box-stove in one corner of the room were long leather boots, thawing in the heat.

"*Ja,* a logging camp is an interesting sight, alright," murmured Papa, as he and Ingrid waited by the Franklin stove until two places were vacant at the table. The men nodded at Papa, for he had been one with them in past winters. Ingrid was proud that he had risen in rank to that of a mail carrier.

Jojo, here we have men of all kinds—loggers, sawyers, swampers, cant-hook men, cooks, and helpers in the kitchen called 'cookees,'" explained Papa.

From the camp window rose mountains of huge log piles, trees that had been hewn and hauled out of the endless forest.

"Look at all those logs," exclaimed Ingrid, forgetting her shyness. "What ever will they do with them?"

Then Papa began the story of destiny. "When a large pine is cut, and about to fall to the ground, someone yells 'timber' at the top of his voice. That is to warn the men of the danger of being struck. When it has fallen, swampers log off the branches. When spring comes, the logs are dragged by teams of horses to the banks of the Great Lake. Here the logs are branded with the marks of the owners. Then they are rolled on skidways from the high banks into the basin of the Great Lake. It is the largest splash you ever heard." Ingrid remembered the sound. "Here in the lake they are arranged in large floats and towed by a tug all the way to the harbor. Men with cant hooks jump from log to log, watching that they don't jam up on each other. Once in the harbor, they wait their turn to be drawn up into the mill where they are sliced lengthwise into lumber by the big saw. Well, you remember the rest of the story." Ingrid recalled the Sunday evening several years before when they had walked the tramway as they went to church. She had often seen the tall walls of lumber which rose on both sides.

"Oh, what a lot a tree has to go through," she sighed.

"*Ja,* that you can say. So when you see a big city go up against the sky, just remember they are using trees like we have here to build their towers and factories. Such is the way of earth." There was a little sadness in the last words.

Ingrid's thoughts grew big. The way of earth—she recalled the butchering season in the late fall and all the changes an animal goes through before it is served in delectable form on platters at the table. The way of earth.

Just then one of the camp men beckoned to Papa to take his place at the table. He had finished his meal, and beside his chair was a vacant place for Ingrid. Papa bowed his head in prayer and began eating his beans and salt pork. Ingrid, so intrigued by new discoveries and new people, almost forgot about her thimble box rolled up in a fascinator in her lap.

That noon she did not have to make any thimble speech. Word passed around that the mail driver's daughter was selling *fingerborgar.* Papa must have whispered to someone, for one after another of these burly, unshaved loggers came to Ingrid with their dimes and nickels. They were not unfriendly people. One could see good in their faces even though they were rough and somewhat unkempt. It came easy to sell thimbles amid their jokes and laughter. When Ingrid and Papa left the camp, two dozen thimbles had been sold.

"Now you will visit the Finnish homes," said Papa, as they drove down to the little dwellings along the lake. "Thimbles sell well in Cranberry."

Pointing with his finger, he called off the owners of the shacks standing in the winter silence of a sunny afternoon. "Over there is Reipi's house, in the next one live the Jakilas, and then Karvalos." They all sounded alike to Ingrid.

The threshold of every hut was scrubbed clean as the snow beside it. Fresh balsam branches were tucked in, forming a perfect doormat for snowy boots. "Poor but clean are the Finns in Cranberry," people said.

"Begin now at Mrs. Torpa's house," suggested Papa, pointing to a tarpaper shack close on the shore.

With that Ingrid was left on her own while Papa went about attending to other matters.

Ingrid knocked on the door of the frugal, one-roomed house which was the Torpas' home, and even before the door opened she could hear women going strong in an unknown language, greasy with r's. "Set your face as a flint," she said to herself.

Her knock must have been mistimed, for when Mrs. Torpa opened the door her large face didn't conceal her annoyance. They must have heard the mail carrier's girl was in their parts selling something. In the spotlessly clean room which was living room, bedroom, and kitchen, all in one, sat four neighbor women busily knitting long, woolen stockings, their needles clicking accompaniment to their unintelligible chatter. On the edge of the bed sat an old grandma smoking a long-stemmed pipe that reached down to her lap. It must have come with her from Finland. Ingrid felt she was an intruder. There was no mistake about it from the way some of them looked at her, and then at each other, as they jabbered something she couldn't understand. "She needs to get experience meeting people," Mama had said. Ingrid wondered what good, in the big world, would come from this social adventure.

The afternoon sun was streaming through the west window of the large room, and the smell of bread in the baking was pleasant enough, but the atmosphere was strange until Ingrid's eyes fell on the youngest woman in the group. She must have been the Mrs. Mielki Papa had talked about. She had come to Cranberry as a bride some months before and was having a lonely time of it. Ingrid felt sorry for this beautiful woman. To think she had to be washed up on these isolated shores. She did not seem to belong in this stern, rugged setting.

When Ingrid had finished her thimble speech, Mrs. Torpa snatched a thimble from her box and tossed it lightly in her hand to determine its weight.

"Scr-rap," she said, in coarse voice, and laid it back in the box.

Ingrid was humiliated. Scrap—that's what people said in Swedish when something was cheap or no good. But they didn't roll so many r's. Mrs. Torpa resumed her Finnish mutterings, and Ingrid stood by the door feeling as she had outside of Mrs. Brask's gate in town. "Hard things make strong character," Mama often said. This was one of those moments called "hard." How strong does one have to get!

But the beautiful Mrs. Mielki didn't let her suffer too long. She took a dime from her purse and came over to Ingrid. In a kind, English tone she said, "It's just what I have been needing." Ingrid felt a new kind of warmth, the kind that draws tears. Mrs. Mielki must have seen a bewildered girl trying to piece out the meanings of life and people and not making much headway.

Ingrid didn't count the clean thresholds she and her thimbles crossed that January afternoon. There were such funny names. But her box of thimbles became lighter and her money bag heavier as she walked from door to door. When she met Papa at the post office and started on the long journey home, her heart was light and her mind well packed with the substance called "memories."

"How many thimbles have you left now?" asked Papa, as they were leaving the little hamlet whose windows reflected the gold of the late afternoon sun.

Ingrid opened her box and showed him. There cuddled up in one corner lay one lone thimble. Papa smiled.

By the time the month of January was torn from the calendar Ingrid had her mouse gray coat. "Never again melton," said Mama. Melton was a fleecy, loosely woven fabric that made the garment look like a bathrobe after some months of wear. "Never again melton. *Ja,* we live and learn."

But the thimble-selling days soon slipped into the annals of the past. Ingrid had seen a cross section of life. There would forever remain a bitter-sweet feeling—life's choicest kind of feeling—from selling ten dozen thimbles from door to door to many kinds of people. But $3.98 had been saved from Papa's check, a nest egg for the dream she held close to her breast.

16. THE NEW SCHOOL

Time passes, and who can stop the stream of years? On the growing settlement snows have fallen, springs have budded, and summers ripened into autumn fields of yellow harvests. Man can now begin to sit back under his own fruitful vine, surveying his growing fields and herds and feeling a little more secure, a little more independent, and even a little arrogant at times.

And over in the little town something great has happened. A large white schoolhouse looks proudly over land and sea—a mighty fortress to behold. From every direction for many miles its splendor meets the traveler's eye.

But think what a struggle there had been! Many town meetings, many protests, many brittle words with long life.

"Consolidated school, of all things! Weren't the little one-room schools along the country roads good enough to learn the children how to read and write?"

"There's no word for such outlandish waste, pouring blood money into a school!"

"Better spend money to improve the farms and raise more cattle!"

"And teach the kids to work. When they finish sitting on the school bench, they cannot even milk a cow. No, sir—a profitless investment."

It happened that a speaker had come to town, a gentleman he was from all appearances. There was a goodly number out that night, and as he spoke of all the advantages of having one large, well-equipped school instead of several, there was much muttering in the group.

"You mean that children scattered all over the settlement are all to come to one schoolhouse?" asked Knut Erickson, rising up right in the middle of the speaker's talk.

The speaker mentioned school rigs gathering up the children who lived outside of town itself. School rigs with canvas tops for shelter, something like the covered wagons in the frontier days. "It will open new jobs for men who need work," he reasoned.

"School rigs!" shouted Gustaf Larson. "*Jojomen.* Now the kids are to ride to school in a school rig. Sit all day in school, then sit again in comfort to and from. What have they got legs for anyhow? They should see how we had it in our youth back in Sweden."

"Oh, you should talk!" It was Papa Hanson's turn to rise, and he was not so little hot. "You, Gustaf, with your Guernsey cows and tractor, always improving yourself with worldly goods. Your treasure is your pocketbook. What about putting something worthy into your children's minds and souls if, indeed, you do not care for it yourself? Always the everlasting pocketbook." With that Papa sat down, already mindful he had said too much.

Papa would never forget that winter night and the storm of opposition that had broken loose in the Town Hall. Men went home with fire in their breasts. He would never forget his own walk home that arctic night. He knew no fire in his breast. His was an iceberg. If only he had kept his temper down! If only he had stated his meaning in a gentler way! *Ja, ack.* That temper, how it springs up every now and then only to crush the best that has been won inside. And as he walked the Corduroy Road, the wind tore at his overcoat and tugged at the lighted lantern in his hand. Shrill screams filled the voids between the willow bushes. *Ack,* it was bleak—*dystert.*

All at once a fierce blast swept across the marsh and snuffed out the light he had in his lantern, and he was left in midnight darkness. Oh, there was winter in his heart, you may well know. He wondered if this little incident should have some meaning. Was it a symbol of defeat—a foreshadowing of a dream that never was to see fulfillment? A cold chill gripped his very bones. *Ja,* think. How he had striven for goals that would bring better opportunities for the ones who were to open doors in the tomorrows!

"*Ja*—all takes time," he said aloud, under the midnight sky, and glad to come off the Corduroy Road into the haven of the forest. No, he would not give up. Perhaps the snuffed-out lantern had no significance after all, though strange it was, indeed. If only he had kept his temper!

And time it took. They that live in one age only are slow to yield. But then there are those with longer vision and deeper insight. Always there are the few. And in the end they win the battle.

So day by day it rose in splendor, the schoolhouse in the upper end of town. And when the last far echoes of the hammer ceased, it stood triumphant—the greatest landmark on the south-shore coast for many a mile. And from the steamer's deck out on the billowy lake it rose as a monument to human strength and perseverance.

So, like all storms, there comes a time of calm. Oh, there may come a lighter breeze that has yet a little word to say, but finally it, too, must yield. And who did not delight to climb the schoolhouse stairs, flight after flight, to reach the spacious garret. And then ascend, with awe and careful step, the last high stairway to the lofty tower! It seemed like climbing to the very stars!

Ack, what one saw from this high cupola! A great experience to have climbed the stairs to such delight. No settler, man or child, would want to miss this high adventure. And should a visitor chance to come to town, he must, of course, make the climb to the high belfry to look in wonder at the grandeur of the countryside, for here, unrolled, lay the vast chart of creation—its hills, lake, rivers, fields, and forests. Ah, it was nothing short of majesty to see! For looking east one saw the hilltop where old Talbot lived and where the sun began to rise. And there were all the clearings, like quilts of green spread between the timbered areas—Larson's, Nelson's, Hammerstrom's, and many others. Even Sofie Monson's log house up among the hills could still be seen though Sofie was no longer there.

And looking west—*ja,* looking west at close of day. *Ack,* what a painting there above the shimmering waters! Sunsets as never seen before. It was enough to call the driest soul to tears and vespers.

Jojo, the matter of the new schoolhouse had its sides alright.

17. The Path Between

That same year Isakson began building his frame house. There was much ado—paper plans, lumber, rafters, bricks, vats of plaster, and people paying visits to the place, days on end. "Go down and take a look at what Isakson is building," they would tell each other. "*Jojomen,* nothing small about them."

"But let us not tear down the log house," pleaded Emma. "So close to my new kitchen door, I can always run in here and live in the warm memories of earlier years. Let it stand, it has much to say to us."

Ja—they could let it stand for a time, thought Isakson. It could have its purpose, at that, though it looked somewhat like a punished dog crouching humbly at the foot of the commanding structure rising alongside of it.

From the little orchard, near the beginning of the

path which led to her neighbor, Mama could see the mounting manor gaining in splendor from day to day. *Ja,* that Isakson, he has it in him, alright. Emma will move like a queen, with an upstairs, four bedrooms, a parlor one won't need to sleep in, and all. Mama looked back at her old log house and sighed. The best she could ever hope for in the uncertain future was a new kitchen in place of the old lean-to and, perhaps, the whole house covered with siding. Log house it would still be, but the logs would be hidden. Then it could be painted. It wouldn't look so meager at that. There would even be a note of prosperity about it, though nothing like the mansion the Isaksons were building.

Upon entering the house, Mama went directly to the bureau drawer and took out the paper sheet on which she had sketched the plans for her own frame house. It had been fun drawing plans, erasing lines, and changing the arrangements of them from time to time. *Ja, ack.* One dreams and plans. And if nothing comes of it, at least you've had the warm, comforting moment of weaving a handsome thread into the fabric of your imagination. Resignedly she lifted the lid on the kitchen stove and laid the crumpled sheet on the flames. "It is not given to all of us to have frame houses," she said, half aloud.

The face of the land was taking on change—more settlers moving in, trails widening into roads, trees being pushed back, and clearings smoothening into large green meadows. Something from the vast outside was moving in.

And now there was talk about closing the path between the Isaksons and Hansons. Some men, called the Town Board, got together and decided to slash out a road for the Hansons along the shore. It would join the main road to town behind the Isaksons without passing the neighbor's door as before. With more people traveling the highways with their horses and wagons, there must be rules and regulations regarding roads. And for all that, Isakson was not for having an established public highway close up on his front-room door. And who can blame him.

But the path between—now it was going to be fenced off. The path that had stood for so much to those who had shared it, that had meant so much to the two women in the early years, the one outlet toward which they could turn their lonely eyes on those long days walled in on all sides by wilderness. How often they had stood at their windows and thought: Maybe someone will come around the bend. . . . Isn't there something fluttering over there in the opening of the woods? . . . I think I see a lantern coming. . . . A path is a hopeful thing.

As far back as Ingrid could remember, the path between the two huts had been one of the warmest fascinations of her young life. She had a curiosity for trails of any kind, whether it was a path tramped by wild deer, the narrow foot trail of a porcupine, or even the tracks a rabbit stitched across the white of a winter woods. A path is a beautiful, curious thing.

"I love to follow a trail just to see what is the reason for it," she told her mother one morning after having discovered a neat hen trail winding into the slough brush behind the chicken house.

"And did you find a reason for it?" asked Mama.

"Yes, I ran smack into the old gray hen you have been missing. She was sitting on a nest of eggs inside of a hollow stump. She clucked at me as if to tell me that this was private property. It was such a cute little spot, hidden among the pussy willow bushes."

But there had been no path so intriguing as the one which led to their neighbor's house. It had widened with the years, giving room for wagon wheels. But now it would soon be closed, and a fence would cross the way.

Mama, too, was sad when she thought about it. Oh, she could still run over to Emma's house for all that, using the new lake road when it was finished. But she would miss the old way. "It's hard to pull up old landmarks by the roots," she said. She remembered that first autumn when the two families came to settle in this pathless wilderness. For a time they tramped the woods between the huts in a strange, indefinite manner, choosing their way where bushes and trees grew thinnest. Then as they grew in dependence on one another, a trail began to fall into shape and became packed and solid by much tramping until it moved in friendly certainty between the two dwellings.

"It's like chapters in a book, this path," Mama said, as one Sunday afternoon she and Ingrid took a walk to the neighbor's house. There was the windswept preface close to the Hanson home; then the shelter of woods where waves and winds were muffled. Midway in the path a wild raspberry patch lay fragrant and warm in August suns. How often they had met here, the women and their little ones, to gather the juicy red fruit for preserving against the winter leanness. What fun were those August afternoons! At the foot of the pines violets and anemones blooming in the spring. In winter an unbroken blanket of snow revealed dozens of unseen creatures that inhabited the woods—raccoons, rabbits, wolves, foxes. Sometimes blood stains could be seen in the snow amid claw marks and feathers—a silent story of the ceaseless way of life, strength overpowering weakness. And as one neared the Isakson house, tall birches marched in rows along the walk which led to Emma's happy kitchen.

From early years the children cherished the wonders which lay along this path. Here they would meet—Annie, Isak, and Ingrid, and later years added others to the group. Here they learned the songs of the robin and meadow lark and other winged creatures that stirred in brush and bush. Here in the spring evenings frogs caroled in the nearby marsh—always the frog song on still evenings in the spring.

"There is so much music along this path," said Ingrid, as they trudged along. An owl sang of faraway things. A small west wind piped a strange minor tune in the tall pines. "It is both happy and sad."

"Yes, the loveliest music is both beautiful and sad. It stirs both feelings. That's what gives you long thoughts and wisdom of the heart." Mama paused to listen to the owl's lament.

"Each season provides its own glory," continued Mama, as she discovered a flaming maple set deep in the green. "This path sings with color when autumn comes. In the spring the air is fragrant with wild cherry bloom; in the summer you catch the breath of raspberries and thimble berries. And through the leafless trees on a winter night a small flame of lamplight points to our neighbor's cabin."

As a young child Ingrid had often stood by the window waiting for that yellow dot of light to come through. Mama remembered a certain winter when that yellow flame shone through many long nights. It was when Isakson lay sick abed and no doctor was to be had. How they had wondered how it would go with Isakson. Night after night Mama had seen that light set deep in the midnight darkness. It had come to symbolize for her many things —the human struggle against great odds . . . courage born from above . . . winter.

Along this trail had been carried rare bits of news from house to house. Shreds of happiness had been flung with the swift wings of a shawl from fireside to fireside. Along its length heavy burdens had been carried by back and shoulders as one sought to aid the other. At times there were burdens which only the heart could carry, but these, too, had to be shared.

Here on a Sunday afternoon in those first summers the two frontier women would sometimes meet and walk together, free for a moment from their many cares. Here they would unveil the many anxious thoughts familiar to womankind, thoughts that press upon the mind and heart. How they had needed each other – lifting, sharing, comforting: "Tomorrow it will be better." Come sickness, childbirth, loneliness, distress, each stood beside the other. Come winter and its snows, or summer and its beauty, the path must be kept open, as open as the door to one another's heart.

But now—subtly, swiftly—a new era is beginning. Like the trees in the forest, which might have wanted to be left alone to preserve their own beauty and strength, the past is being pushed back—the past with all its treasures of the heart. Now there are new people, new roads, new machinery, new ideas. Log cabins are torn down to make room for statelier mansions. Wells are dug, and with them comes a modern device for drawing water called a pump. Even the children can manipulate them. New kitchen stoves called ranges grace the kitchens with their reservoirs and warming ovens and nickel-plated trim. New plows and rakes and cultivators stand gleaming in the fields. *Ja,* think. Surely the world is changing. As Gustaf Larson would say, "Let her go, Gallagher."

And everywhere are fences, drawing lines where farm meets farm and closing off one neighbor from the other.

18. THE MOLINE ORGAN

Down by the shores the Isaksons' large frame house stands complete and beautiful—in full bloom with its porch, and front hall, and boarded sidewalks from each entrance, front and back. *Jojomen,* the Isaksons have it nice.

And can you think, the Hansons have torn down their sagging lean-to and have built a new wing on the old log house! It faces west and brings no end of pleasure as Mama washes dishes by the window facing lakeward. When the log house gets a covering of siding and a coat of paint, it will not look so far behind the times. Be that as it may, should you look inside of Hanson's house you would be surprised.

Jojo, there is something there to talk about.

And the Axelbergs—*ja,* think anyway, the Axelbergs now live three miles from the shores up in the wooded hills. Their little log house looks down into a deep, lush ravine where runs a laughing brook. How Hanna loves that brook! She stands upon her high hill now and greets the morning with her joyous song. And far below the purling brook accompanies her rich soprano voice. A child of a King indeed! And happy she is to have a two-room log house and a forty of wild land coming into their own possession by and by. Life has turned a new leaf for the Axelbergs. The skies are clearing.

But Mama misses Hanna and looks longingly toward the Fishermen's Cottage up along the lake, for Hanna's visits are less frequent now. But even so she walks the three miles to the shores whenever she can. And Mama is not unaware of her coming, for she can hear her song up in the woods long before the fluttering figure appears in the upper clearing. *Ack,* how her song puts morning in one's heart, and when Hanna steps inside the kitchen door, a special kind of sunlight floods the house. It's good to have some Hannas in this world.

And during the past swift years other events have happened to the families on the shore. The Hansons have three more sons. After Anders came Emil. Mama is not so certain about this one. He does not seem to have a bent for land and stumps and plows and stables. He is a dreamer, one can see, with a boundless imagination. *Ja,* Mama wonders about this one. Often she listens to his exaggerated, homespun tales. More than once he has come running in, all out of breath, to inform his family of the large armies he has encountered along the shores.

"Shouldn't wonder if the Spanish-American War left some kind of mark on him," she told Papa one morning at the breakfast table. For during her pregnancy the war, with all its grim aspects, was the main subject of conversation between the settlers. It didn't surprise her when little Emil began early to carry a long stick across his shoulder which he called his gun.

"You talk," said Papa, dismissing the subject with a wave of his hand. "Some old midwife's fable, nothing in it."

And then came George—a lively one, not given to looking vaguely into space. No dreamer this one, but quick to laugh and quick to speak. He might become a good one on the farm.

And last of all came little Teodor. Papa held much converse with the Lord regarding this one, pleading that his youngest son might become a preacher. Among those born on these shores, should there not rise up one to be a servant of the Lord? What greater blessing could one ask?

And in the Isakson home five more are sitting around the family table—Ruth, Ella, Axel, Aldor, and, last of all, the little fair-haired Alma. Eleven there are now, bowing their heads for grace around the evening meal, counting the parents. *Ja,* Isaksons have room for over a dozen. But likely now the families on the shores are quite complete. The older children no longer make barefoot prints on the sands along the shore, for they have reached the age where they must work. The playtime days for them are over. But there will still be castles on the shore and foot and finger patterns engraved deeply in the sands, for Alma and Teodor will play together for some time to come. And good it is to see the marks of little children up along the lake. Realizing their child-bearing days are likely over, Mama and Emma sigh a bit and wonder how it will be when all the imprints which belong to childhood days are washed away. *Ack.*

And so the years have come and gone, and many suns have set across the ruffled waters. Moons have drenched the wilderness with peace, and stars have tugged at all that is immortal in the human breast.

But let us look inside the Hanson home again. Amid the ebb and flow of life a dream has broken through the iron locks and reached fulfillment. A dream fed by hardships and long, patient waiting. And here were tidings which stirred the countryside far and wide. Few events created so much talk from house to house and round the heating stove in Klovstad's store. You never saw the likes of what came to the Hansons' house one sunny summer day! It was something to surprise both old and young! *Jojomen.*

In one corner of their sparsely furnished front room there stands an immense, shining object with a thousand melodies in its breast. Ingrid's dream come true! An organ! A Moline organ! One of the first such wonders on this Wisconsin edge. And on its rack there stands a large gray book with keyboard pictures illustrating how to make music on those lovely, snow-white keys. It shows how to find middle C and to build up thirds to form a chord, and already there is music in the Hanson house. Mama, too, is learning how to chord the simpler songs. And now she sings again. That lovely alto voice she had in the city choir is back once more. My, it is good to sing again! She picks the simple songs which she can handle with but three changes of chords and for which she needs use only the white keys. And then she sings with confidence about the security of God's children—

Tryggare kan ingen vara
Än Gud's lilla barnaskara . . .

Ja, now there is something more to hear than waves and wind.

It was a great day when the Moline organ rolled into town. The mail driver hauled it from the nearest railroad station twenty miles away. People along the way dropped their plows and house tasks and stood wide-eyed with wonder when they saw the enormous box in the wagon, this crated mystery. Slowly it moved along, for this was not an easy load, even with two horses pulling up front.

And when word got out that it was an organ, talk began to spread like forest fire.

"A brand new organ for the Hansons! How out of all reason. An old and used organ would not do. No, it had to be fresh from the factory, and so expensive. How much more sense it would have been to use the money for some needed farm machinery, or two, three cows to increase the herd." So said farmer Bergquist, south of town, as they met, a little group, inside of Klovstad's store.

"And money ahead at that," figured Nelson, as he knocked his pipe against the woodbox near the stove.

"They say the organ costs about eighty dollars."

"*Jo, ja tackar ja.* That Hanson has some strange ideas in his head," said Bergquist, shaking his own head.

"And now that girl of theirs is going to learn to play, and she can't even milk a cow." Per Johnson, too, must add his bit. And then they lit their pipes, and behind the smoke there was a look of confidence in being men of saner judgments. *Nej,* the coming of an organ was no small event.

"That's the way people talked about the new schoolhouse," said Ingrid when the rumors reached her ears one day.

"It takes time, Ingrid," answered Papa. "The worthwhile things in life are slow to be accepted."

But who can know how a twelve-year-old girl feels when a special prayer is answered and a dream becomes reality? The night the organ came she could not sleep. Lying on a cot across from the organ, she saw its splendor through the moonlit room. If she could only unlock its treasure and draw from its shining keys some utterance to the feelings, deep inside, for which there were no human words.

So Ingrid and Mama set to work to learn to chord, choosing the simpler songs. And sing and play they did in the spare moments of the day and in the late of evening when their tasks were done. And it was not unusual to hear bursts of song, here and there, about the Hanson farm. Out in the cornfield, where the boys were weeding, echoes came in whistled tunes. Papa in his wheat field could not restrain the melodies that swelled within his breast. Close by the cabin door birds in the treetops paused to listen, then suddenly broke out in rapturous carolings. A touch of heaven lay upon the Hanson homestead.

But having served its time, the idle talk about the organ lost its zest and reached its ultimate end. There were the few who could not repress their curiosity to see the new instrument and find out how the Hansons were making out in learning to manipulate it. These few got together and planned a visit to the Hansons, a friendly visit only. They would even bring a cake since Mama Hanson might be unprepared.

It was a lovely afternoon when they set off for Hanson's place, and nature had slipped on her autumn dress. And proud Mama was to go to the door and lead them into the sanctity of the front room.

"*Nej, men* can you think!" they exclaimed, before they even crossed the threshold of the room which housed the lovely wonder. Here stood a tall, red case of cherry wood, sparkling in newness, with a row of stops to pull or push, and pedals to tramp and swells to press and fancy carving on the rack and everything. A handsome piece to look at. What must it be to listen to!

"*Ack,* to own a thing like this!" said Klara Larson, Gustaf's wife. "How wonderful must be the tone —will you not play for us so we can hear how it sounds?"

Then Mama beckoned to Ingrid, and though it took all the courage she could muster, Ingrid sat down on the stool and began to chord the song she had practiced many times. Then Mama joined the music with her alto voice.

Tryggara kan ingen vara
Än Gud's lilla barnaskara. . .

As in a spell, the guests around the organ watched and listened. To think how Ingrid handled those white keys! And to hear how Mama's voice blended richly into the chords. *Nej,* now there was no fault to find. They went from Hanson's house, each with a sigh.

"*Ack,* was it not a wonder how she played, that girl of theirs?" said Klara Larson, as they walked the sandy road to where the team of horses stood. "Almost I would sell a couple of cows and buy an organ, a second-hand one, if nothing else."

"Oh, it does something deep inside of you, an uplift to the soul it is. I felt as if I was in second heaven." Anna Johnson came away inspired by the visit.

"My, there is more to life than being practical," said Sofie Monson, as they stepped into the wagon and headed south. "Always we hear them say, 'Be *praktisk,* be wise.' I wonder if it pays to be so wise that one starves the soul."

And what happened after that? Before the following summer had run out a half a dozen organs had rolled into town.

19. From These Shores

The time Mama had long foreseen was finally here, and there was heaviness of heart as she set herself to the tasks of a new day. Again she realized the price one pays for setting roots in a remote corner of earth.

"And—on top of all—it's November," she complained to Papa as she lit the kerosene lamp and then touched the same match to the birch-bark kindling in the cookstove. "Bare trees, gray skies, wind and waves." The sleepy hoarseness in Mama's voice matched her mood.

Papa looked up from the paper he was reading, surprised to see Mama in such low spirits.

"*Ja,* everything has its season," he said. " 'A time to be born and a time to die; a time to plant, and a time to pluck up; a time to weep and a time to laugh.'" Mama detected a minor strain in Papa's voice as he quoted Ecclesiastes. She knew that he, too, had a weight on his heart.

A strange melancholy brooded over the little home on the shores. The children were still under the covers of sleep. Almost you could hear them breathe.

"We'll let them sleep a while longer, it's early," suggested Mama as she blew out the lamp, leaving the faint dawn to process into the full light of another day. The stove sent a red glow into the dusk of the kitchen, and a northwest wind squealed in the stovepipe as they gathered the milk pails and set off for the barn. The Great Lake, which had lain like a shimmering prairie only yesterday, had whipped up a temper during the night and large, frothy billows snarled against the land. There was a new kind of sadness about, different from any Papa and Mama had ever experienced—and they had tasted many varieties. So much had been torn away from them.

And now this. Ingrid was leaving home. They had seen it coming—the first bird to depart from the family nest, from now on to flight her own wings into the unknown tomorrows. For weeks Mama had previewed the day when she must tear herself loose from her firstborn. In her imagination she had seen her child set off on the far journey, waving her last farewell at the lonely first bend in the road, then disappearing from sight. She had visualized her own loneliness as she turned back into the emptiness of the house and began gathering up the many reminders, pulling from the table the vacant chair and trying to close her ears to the echoes of the missing voice. She was going over it all as she tramped the well-worn path to the stable, the clink of the milk pails accenting each step.

Dawn was trying hard to blossom into a sunrise when Ingrid came down from her little room in the attic a half-hour later. She was happy for the promise it held. This day could stand a little sunshine. For this was the morning of that tomorrow of which she had long dreamed. She was starting off for the Big City. Here she hoped to find the magic trail that would lead to the great highway of life. Contrary to the usual rural pattern of her day, she was not going to the city to find housework. She was going on to school, to glean a simple education that would qualify her to teach in some remote rural outpost.

"Just like the Hansons," people said. "Spend money on education, and the girl can't even milk a cow."

It had been Papa's and Mama's hope that Ingrid should have the advantage of going on to school, though how it was to be accomplished was another matter. "But 'comes the day, comes a way,'" said Mama, as they considered the difficulties involved and their own financial limitations. They knew it was largely up to Ingrid herself. If, in her spare hours, she were able to work for her board and room during the school year and take on extra studies during the summer months, it might be possible that in two years of normal school training she could acquire a third-grade certificate. This would permit her to teach all grades from first to eighth in some one-room country school. Once having reached this goal, the way would be open for further training and larger fields of service.

But to Ingrid the choosing of a vocation was no small matter, even though there seemed to be but two choices for a girl, unless she married very young and settled on a piece of land. She must either become a hired girl and know how to keep her place or, with utmost determination and hard work, prepare herself to teach a motley group of boys and girls in some gray, belfried building along a lonely country road. But Ingrid had felt another urge, had nursed another dream. What about that reed organ which had been purchased at such a sacrifice? She was not content to merely chord her way. This did not satisfy the hunger that lay locked within. If she could only study music!

"Music! *Ja,* think anyway—what kind of ambition is that for a poor man's daughter?" folks had said. "That's no job at all and no money in it. Just a little pleasure, one of life's side-lines. *Nej, tacka vet ja,* to find some steady work as hired girl where you can make up to $3.50 a week, with board and room besides, that's the thing to do. One must be *praktisk.*"

And so they offered their generous advice but understood so little.

Ja, Ingrid would prepare to be a country teacher. But since she had heard there was a piano in the city home where she was to stay while going to school, she still dared to dream. Perhaps—oh, was it too much to hope?—perhaps she could find a way to take some lessons. Only a few, perhaps; she would work so hard to pay for them. How she would surprise the folks back home when she returned!

Yesterday she had pulled out Papa's Swedish

satchel that had lain crumpled under the rafters ever since the Big City Conference years ago. It was an unusual satchel. If you pushed out all the folds, you discovered an unbelievable amount of room inside. Her simple wardrobe would not begin to fill it. It was like the life before her, so much to fill and so little to put into it. The old satchel had seen its day, coming as it had from Sweden to America and finally to these shores. It looked old and tired, and the folds had grown brittle, ready to crack if you pressed against them.

Evening had come early yesterday. When her packing was finished and the supper dishes had been put away, she stole down to the familiar shores where, through the years, she had so often spent an hour in the evening. Young or old, there comes a time for being alone, and each one seeks his sanctuary of stillness where he can think and listen, think and see. As Ingrid sat beside the quivering waters, the sounds of evening muted, her thoughts became solemn and touched with sadness. Was she really going to leave these shores where her roots had already been set so deeply?

It was with pride that she had unfolded her plan of going away to Annie and Isak and her friends at school. It seemed an heroic thing, this stepping out of the seclusion of the backwoods into larger populated places. She felt a certain glow surrounding the very telling of it.

But now she wasn't so sure. A door seemed to be closing, as if she faced an abyss between herself and what would never be again. Something was slipping away. It was like pulling out from shore, seeing the coastline recede and, little by little, fade from sight. Was life like this?

Childhood yesterdays came rolling back. What was it Papa had once said when she was a little girl and the waves had washed away her towers in the sand?

"It is the towers that are built within our hearts that count. These we take with us into the days ahead. No waves can wash away the spires of the soul."

Spires?—*torn,* Papa called them. Ingrid was too young to understand what Papa had said that morning while they sat together on a log, the waves purling against the pebbles and stones on shore. But this evening, as she sat alone, she understood. These towers of which he spoke—what else could they be but the sacred memories one stores away, memories pointing to the stars, memories that have the power to live, to shed their sunset colorings on days ahead?

Ingrid's country-fed thoughts rolled back to the tender years of early childhood. Just then from some dark corner in the grasses of the Big Slough a loon began to cry. A loon's sad, intriguing song. It touched a deep well in her being, and instantly she felt a familiar floodtide of emotion rendering her capable not only of remembering, but of feeling, hearing, re-experiencing, a certain vibrating moment in her life. Cradled in her memory was a hushed evening in her early childhood when Mama had taken her in her lap and had sung the Swedish lullaby, the one she loved so much. It was about calling the lambs—calling them home, for it was night.

Lammena, lammena, lammena mina små,
Kom hem i kväll, fåren också.

Nestled in Mama's arms, feeling that warm sense of security which one can know but once, she could see through the open door a little sailboat coming into port. She should hear the last tired chirp of a bird returning to its nest. Across the vast waters foghorns called sleepily to other foghorns. And from somewhere in the great marsh came the lonely cry of a loon. A loon's lament. Somehow it belonged to the evening. It belonged to time; it belonged to her life.

How warm and tender were Mama's arms as long straying thoughts began to taper into sleep. And all was well with the world—the lambs secure in the fold . . . the ship safe in the haven . . . the bird content in the shelter of its nest . . . and a loon pouring out the feel of the forever into the night. A moment never to be washed away.

Ingrid began to realize that her childhood had many significant moments — God-given ones they were—which now seemed to rise like mountain peaks in the distance. They would ever challenge her to reach out for the highest, to lift her eyes upward. She glanced across the waters of the Great Lake. Darkness had settled, and the fine thread of light on the horizon smiled back at her. How these lights had spoken to her young life! How much which had affected her life had come from this great body of water which lay before her. It stood for many things —life, death, peace, struggle, eternity. As far back as she could remember, here was the field which always provided illustrations for the songs and prayers and sermons heard in loghouse prayer meetings or in the little red church in town. Here were the storms that Jesus stilled, the waters on which he walked, the shores from which he called to fishers, "Come, follow me, and I will make you fishers of men." Here was the dark, stormy Jordan man must cross to ultimately reach the Eternal City whose far-off thread of light was ever beckoning.

Ingrid became suddenly aware of how deep was the kinship between herself and this lake. "These are my shores," she whispered into the ears of night.

There were many other scenes that came to her remembrance as she sat on the driftwood log beside the prattling waves—the playtime haunts along the path between neighbors . . . Hanna's song ringing through the woods . . . Cranberry . . . ten dozen thimbles . . . the Moline organ.

Above all, she could never forget a certain Sunday evening that swelled into a moment of heaven when the cadence of a certain song flowed into her heart, into the night, into the whole universe. Three eternal words. She would hear them always; she would cling to them forever—*fräst av nåd,* saved by grace.

Reluctantly, she rose to go back to the house. A full moon had come up over the Big Pine and the night wind piped its usual nocturne. It was beautiful out here. But when this night was over, there would begin a new chapter in her life, a new tomorrow. She would be leaving home in the morning.

Ingrid noticed a light in the front room window of her home and knew that the best lamp had been lit. It was time for family vespers. She paused to look once more upon the log house with its covering of siding. Some day it would crumble; the tall trees surrounding it would grow old and yield to the might of the winds; the land would pass into other hands. *Ack*, time and change!

But something was hers to keep. Along with her Swedish bag, she would carry an invisible satchel filled with something that would consistently bloom, memories that would soften, lift, and shed courage on the days ahead. No waves of life could wash away the spires from these shores.

GLOSSARY

Ack	Alas
Ack, ja	Alas, yes
Apelsiner	Oranges
Å så väva vi vamman *Å så slå vi tillsamman*	Thus we are weaving home-spun Thus we pound it together.
Blåst å böljor	Winds and waves
Du gamla, du fria, du fjäll-höga nord	Thou ancient, thou glorious, thou high-mountained North
Dystert	Bleak
Enbärsdricka	Juniper ale
Fingerborgar	Thimbles
Fram en suck sig smyger *Hörd av ingen vän* *Dock lik duvan flyger* *Den mot himmelen*	A sigh steals forth Unheard by anyone Yet like a dove it flies Up toward heaven.
Fy	Ugh!
Frälst av nåd	Saved by grace
Följetång	Serial
God dag	Good day; hello
Grönsaker	Vegetables
Guds nåd	God's grace
Han som hänger i vinner	He who hangs on wins.
Hundvalp	Puppy

Ja	Yes
Ja, du stora värld	Well, of all things!
Ja, men i all världens tider	Who in the world?
Ja, men se	Yes, but look
Jaså	Oh! Indeed!
Ja, tacka för de	Yes, of course
Ja visst	Certainly
Jo, ja tackar ja	Well, I should say so
Jojo	Indeed
Jojomen	Yes, sir! Yes, indeed!
Jojomen! För all del	Yes, sir! I should say so.
Jul	Christmas
Julotta	Early service on Christmas Day
Kalas	Party
Kalvdans	Veal loaf
Korv	Sausage
Kringlor	Double-ring twist-biscuits
Kära hjärtans	My goodness
Lammena, lammena, lammena mina små Kom hem i kväll, fåren också	Lambs, my little lambs, Come home tonight.
Men kära hjärtans	Dear me! Isn't that something!
Morgonstund har guld i mun	The morning hours have gold in the mouth. (The early bird gets the worm.)
Nej	No
Nej du	No, sir.

Nej, du, lejonen ville inte ha han	No, the lions didn't want him.
Nej, för all del	No, indeed not
Nej, tack	No thanks
Nej, tacka vet ja	I'd much rather
Nåden	Grace
Om or *men*	Ifs or buts
Ombyte förnöjer	A change is pleasant.
Ont i magen	Stomach ache
Palt	Black pudding
Praktisk	Practical
Pressylta	A pressed, jellied meat loaf
Ruter	Spunk
Röra	Mess
Sabbatsdag, hur skön du är	Sabbath day, how lovely thou art.
Sjung	Sing
Slarv	Frivolity
Smörgås	Sandwich
Stuga	Cottage
Syltor	Jellied meat loaf of various kinds
Tofflor	Shoes
Torn	Spires
Tryggare kan ingen vara Än Guds lilla barnaskara	More secure is no one ever Than the loved ones of the Savior.
Tuktomästaren	Strict taskmaster

Uti storm vi stå *Snart vi sälla hamnen nå*	We ride out the storm Soon we reach the blissful shore.
Var inte för glad, du	Don't be too happy.
Var så god	Please
Vem ska ta emot prästen?	Who is going to entertain the preacher?
Vi får lära oss sätta mun efter matsäcken	We must learn to adjust our appetites to our feedbags.
Välling	Gruel